BENNY:

The Biography of a Horse

BENNY:

The Biography of a Horse

BY NORMA CLINE KLOSE

Drawings by Gloria Gaulke

Lothrop, Lee & Shepard Co., Inc.
NEW YORK

CONTENTS

Getting Acquainted   7

Benny Plays a Trick   16

Unwelcome Gifts   29

Snowbound   35

Three's a Crowd   53

Reckless Rider   64

No Hobbles for Benny   77

Homecoming   85

Parade Plans   95

Gone!   112

The Search   120

Benny in Training   131

The 4-H Show   141

The Winners   152

Grandpa   164

Struggle for Life   169

ONE

Getting Acquainted

Benny's eyes were small; his lower lip drooped. Both were indications of meanness and laziness. But Ben was neither: he never intentionally kicked at a person or threw a rider. His chest was narrow and his legs were short. His pasterns were not so long and sloped nor so angled as they should have been for speed and stamina. His wind was poor. Yet he could run faster for a short distance than many a Quarter Horse; he could run all day if there was another horse to overtake.

Worst of all, his disposition was not the kind looked for in a horse to be ridden by children. Benny was everything the horse books said he shouldn't be. On top of that he was old.

He was beautiful.

He became a member of our family in 1945 when he was about seventeen years old. We were already boarding a horse when our neighbors, the Gerry Fauths, asked us to take Benny. We couldn't have turned them down because we had plenty of room in our big old barn. But the clinching reason was that my two brothers, Howdy and Earl, wanted another horse so they could ride together.

I was only nine that summer and considered neither old nor strong enough to learn to ride. But I loved Benny from the day he walked into our barnyard and I loved to hear Mr. Fauth tell stories about Benny's life.

Benny was born a wild colt somewhere in the southwest. He roamed hills and plains for several years before his herd was rounded up by one of the large cattle ranchers. He was branded, quickly broken to bit and saddle, gelded, and trained as a cow pony. His reflexes were superb. His alertness must have been born of those years of being wild, for I never saw a barn-bred horse that could equal it. Because of his short legs Benny could turn sharply and stop suddenly even when galloping full speed, perfect qualities for a cow pony.

He was efficient and hard-working until he began to lose his wind. Then he was shipped east to Michigan with nineteen other aging cow ponies for quick sale.

The Fauths bought Benny and he had a happy life with them for several years, until they sold their lovely old place in Fenton and moved to Flint, a city too large, and with acreage too small, to care for a horse. The Fauths wanted a good home for their beloved Benny, so they gave him to us.

Earl and Howdy really learned to ride on Benny. After the first summer he was our only horse, and they took turns on him or sometimes rode him double. But as they grew older and their interests changed, they rode him less and less. Sports and other high school activities did not leave them much time.

I waited impatiently for the day when I could learn to ride. And I had to wait two whole years. Grandpa Cline was my first instructor and he began by mounting old Ben himself so that I could see how it was done. There was no saddle and Benny's bridle was put together out of old leather straps and a snaffle bit with no curb. The reins were two old pieces of rope.

While Grandpa jogged around the barnyard, I couldn't help noticing, even in my nervousness, the

9

proud way Benny carried himself. He arched his neck, picked up his legs, and was quick to respond to Grandpa's slightest command.

When Grandpa dismounted and prepared to give me a leg up, I patted Ben on the nose and looked into his dark eyes—intelligent, mischievous and sly eyes, but smiling and good-humored.

"Oh, Benny," I pleaded as Grandpa hoisted me up, "please don't mind if I'm nervous. I'm not a good rider yet but I will be someday, if you'll let me."

Grandpa handed the rope reins to me and Ben immediately stepped forward, slowly taking me through the gate to the pasture.

"There's nothing to it," I thought. "He's going to obey me just the way he did Grandpa."

Elated over my initial success, I relaxed the tension in my back and arms, gave Ben a joyful pat under his mane, and urged him gently into his comfortable canter.

But Ben mistook relaxation for confidence: here was his chance to show a new rider his spirit. He leapt forward in a full gallop. Surprised and terrified, I grabbed his mane with my left hand while pulling back on the reins for some control with my right. When there was no response, I knew there was no possible way I could stop him. I gripped my legs tight to his sides. Tears, either from fear or wind, I couldn't tell which, came to my eyes as we raced headlong for the ravine at the end of the pasture. I was afraid to let go my hold on his mane. At the same time, I knew that if I didn't turn him, *he* would jump the ravine and *I* wouldn't.

I had almost decided to let myself fall off but then, suddenly, I couldn't. If I did, I realized, I would never get on his back again.

Fortunately, Benny was galloping in a straight line, parallel to the fence by the road. If he had swerved at all, I would have fallen off. I gingerly loosened the grip of my left hand in his mane, grabbed the knotted rope reins, and swung my arm cautiously in an attempt to neck-rein him away from the ravine which now seemed only a few feet away.

Benny turned so sharply, he nearly threw me. But I regained my balance after a momentary jerk while Benny slowed to a canter. He continued swinging in a big arc until he was heading back for the barn. I could see Grandpa in the distance under the old walnut tree but I was too far away to see his expression. (I know now that he was concerned and amused.)

Benny hesitated for an instant when I tried to slow him to a walk by pressure on the bit but he seemed to be enjoying himself so much that instead of a walk he broke into a gallop again. With the barn ahead, I felt secure and exhilarated. I even exulted for a moment in the power of the muscles beneath me.

The ground passed under Ben's flying hooves in a

blur, but the white barn and Grandpa grew larger and clearer. Benny never slackened his speed, even when it seemed as though we would gallop right through the barnyard fence. Both my hands once again had a firm hold in his mane, since I knew trying to pull back on the reins would be no use.

I stiffened my back and arms, getting ready for the unavoidable crash through the fence, when Benny suddenly straightened his forelegs and dug his hind legs into the dirt. He slid to a dusty stop directly in front of Grandpa, and I finished that ride on Ben's neck.

Then I was on the ground, with my arms around Benny, sobbing into his mane, "I didn't fall off, I didn't fall off, I didn't fall off!"

Grandpa silently removed Ben's bridle. Ben threw up his head, pulled back from me, and ambled slowly into the pasture to graze. He acted bored.

"Norma, my girl," Grandpa said, "that was the best job of riding I have *ever* seen. Benny gave you a real ride, all right, but you stayed on, you stuck to him like a piece of gum."

Grandpa's very blue eyes showed his approval of my behavior on a ride that seemed to me to have lasted an hour but was in fact only a few minutes. His approval also quieted my shaky knees.

"Oh, Grandpa, I'm so glad I didn't fall off! But how am I ever going to be able to keep Ben from running away with me?" I asked.

"Norma Jean," he answered, "the ride you took on Ben today told me a couple of things about you." Grandpa and I walked slowly into the barn. I wasn't quite sure what he was going to say but I knew that if anyone could help me win Benny over, Grandpa could.

Grandpa lowered himself onto a bale of straw and put a plug of *Mail Pouch* chewing tobacco into his mouth. I sprawled out on my stomach on a nearby bale, leaning on my elbows with my chin in my hands, waiting attentively for Grandpa to continue.

"After a ride like the one you just took, I see that you're not afraid of Benny and that you still want him as your own."

He said this pretty much as a question but apparently he didn't need an answer, for he went on to say, "Benny's a cantankerous old animal, like I am sometimes. I know, though, that with lots of patience and hard work, you'll have him following you around like a pet monkey. Now, he's not a young colt, so don't expect to teach him any high falutin' circus tricks. But he's not too old for you. He's got lots of spunk and spirit. You'll want him to keep that, 'cause it's not much fun riding a lazy old plug."

I nodded eagerly.

"He's certainly not too old, even though right now he's at an age when most horses are beyond good use—even as a pet. Why, he has a constitution that's stronger than mine."

I half giggled because he was always making comparisons like that between himself and any animal he happened to be talking about.

"What we'll do first," Grandpa went on, "is to get you a better bridle. Benny has a hard mouth, so any weak bit without a curb strap would do no good at all on that stubborn horse. You found that out today. He obeyed me because my arms are stronger than yours and I weigh a lot more than you do, so he's got just a little more respect for me right now."

"Do you think I can do it, Grandpa? I mean, he's the best horse in the whole world and I want to be able to ride him and have fun with him and show him off. How long do you think it will take?" How anxious I was to be able to parade Benny in front of friends!

"I suspect it won't take long, once we get a better bridle on him. And you won't need a saddle. Learning to ride bareback will be best for you. You'll be able to develop such a good seat and balance that it'll be hard for him to shake you off, even if he should take a mind to. You and Benny will learn to understand each other. You'll tell him what you want through the pressure of your legs. And your hands will be free, so you won't have to grab any old saddle horn to hold on. That way you'll keep in touch with his mouth, gently but firmly. But he'll figure you out in his own way. He'll try you out lots of times."

I listened raptly while Grandpa went on giving me more information. When, finally, he left to throw some ears of corn to our Herefords, I lay on my bale of straw a while longer, dreaming of the time when I would take Benny for long rides and we would be in complete harmony with each other.

TWO

Benny Plays a Trick

Michigan summers can sometimes be unbearably hot and humid and this was one of the worst. Most of the cattle were lying motionless in the shade of the oak trees, their only movement the chewing of cuds and the twitching of ears and tails to get rid of the flies which pestered them. The pigs found relief in the cool mud where they'd sometimes lie in one spot until the sun went down. The bantam chickens did their scratching inside the barn, looking for delectable insects in the loose straw.

On very hot days, I would find Ben under the old walnut tree in the barnyard next to the watering

trough where he kept himself busy switching his long
black tail to flick the flies away from his flanks and
legs. He would stop frequently to duck his head into
the cool fresh water to the level of his eyes. He would
graze in the lush pasture only in the early morning,
at dusk, or whenever there happened to be a breeze.

And Benny invariably found me perched on top of
the white barnyard fence. Occasionally, I shared my
breakfast toast and raspberry jam with him, or a
banana—he would eat almost anything. But most of
the time, I silently chewed a wisp of hay, admiring
Benny.

I'd talk with Benny about everything, even problems. And somehow answers came much more easily

to me after a "discussion" with Benny than they did otherwise. He was my best and most sympathetic listener for many summers.

Grandpa was able to get a fine bridle with long leather reins. The low curb bit had medium shanks with a leather strap which meant more control and no yanking.

When Grandpa boosted me up on Benny's back for the second time, Ben felt at once the new self-confidence flowing through my arms and legs and was aware of the change in the bit. But because Benny was Benny, he didn't balk at the curb. He seemed as eager as I was to get going. His head came up and his ears went forward. He tucked his chin in proudly, arching his spotted neck.

He couldn't stand quietly, waiting for me to make myself comfortable. He began to move easily at a mincing jog, carrying me into the same pasture where he had had his fun with me on our first ride. He jogged quickly along the path the cattle had made by the fence, seeming not to pay any particular attention to me, yet alert to every movement I made.

We began a zigzag course back and forth across the pasture as I tested his obedience to the reins and as I adjusted myself to his jerky trot. We moved through the thick grass in complete harmony, understanding each other more with each passing minute. Though it was in the back of my mind, not once did Benny make a move that might make me think he'd take his head and break into a wild gallop as he had on my first ride.

No, Benny reveled in the delights of the summer afternoon and I reveled in the joy of riding Benny.

After a few days of riding in the spacious pastures, we were allowed to range a little farther afield. Our farm was beautiful. It had the right setting for every wild west story I could invent: the rolling hill pastures south of Cook Road behind the big old barn became the Rocky Mountains; the drainage ditch in the lower pastures was the Rio Grande, which could be safely crossed only over a wooden bridge because the mud was too deep to ride through. The "badlands" were on the south side beyond the drainage ditch to the boundary of the next farm and were almost inaccessible, nearly overgrown with high brush and weeds.

The big white farmhouse with its dark green shutters stood directly across Cook Road from the barn. The red brick front porch complemented the flat face of the old house. What had once been an old tool shed tacked on to the back of the house was converted into a large recreation room. Many of the window panes were so old that trees and people and moving cars seen through them looked wavy and jagged. Mom never had those old panes replaced; they were part of the charm of this hundred-year-old house.

The large front yard was rimmed with very old maple trees and two pine trees. Mom tended the shrubbery along the front of the house, but it was Earl and Howdy's job to keep the grass cut and watered so that even during dry spells in summer the lawns never looked scorched.

The side yards were flanked by orchards. Every

spring we had masses of blossoms and bothersome honey bees; every summer and fall we had mountains of apples, pears, peaches, and plums.

The gravel driveway on the east side had been extended into a two-track dirt trail by Grandpa who drove twice a day from his little house to the barn to do chores. For a reason we could never fathom, Grandpa chose to drive across the fields rather than on the smoother gravel roads—the distance was exactly the same—despite the mud in the rain, the dust in the heat, and the drifts of snow in the winter.

The rest of the farm ran for many acres north of Cook Road. And it was on these flatter fields and thick woods that Benny and I now concentrated. We had exhausted most of the possibilities of the south end; the "old West" was pretty free now of outlaws and cattle thieves. It was "the Plains" which captivated us. Grandpa's private road became an Indian trail or the tracks made by covered wagons. Here pioneers had fought their way bravely through Iroquois, Apaches or Sioux. Benny and I protected the corn fields, the wheat fields, the oat fields and the alfalfa fields, frightening away at least half a million Indians a day. Other days, we would chase outlaws, horse thieves, bank robbers or kidnapers as far back as the woods, which eventually came to be a thriving mining town in the "old West."

On one of these forays, Benny played a mean trick on me. It was my first discovery that all Benny's traits were not admirable.

That particular August afternoon was very hot. I had intended to stay in the cool house looking through the *Horseman's Encyclopedia*, but by the middle of the afternoon, I became more and more restless. I realized that next week I would be starting back to school and my long daily rides would come to an end. That decided me. I would go for another ride while I could, in spite of the heat.

It took only a few minutes to lure Benny from his cool spot under the walnut tree. As I slipped his bridle on, I worked out a plan to have the dishonest sheriff of the mining town in the woods ousted from his job and jailed. Only then would the town again be prosperous and safe. Ben and I would hunt him down. We would become famous—the only horse and girl-rider team ever to have saved innocent miners and their families from the clutches of an evil sheriff.

We cantered along the hilly trail toward the woods, our eyes peeled for the sheriff, but soon Benny began sweating hard and I was quickly losing my enthusiasm for the game. My clothes stuck to me and the heat of Benny's body was like a radiator against my legs. But

I didn't want to turn back. Benny might sense that I had made a mistake in starting out at all and I might lose control of him.

I decided to go to the woods. Perhaps it would be cooler there.

We left the trail, cantered across an alfalfa field, and Benny slowed to a jog because of the tangle of prickly bushes at the entrance to the woods. I let him jog. We made our way along the narrow path, cautiously avoiding low-hanging branches, and I brought Benny to a stop close to the far side of the woods. His neck was lathered from my unmerciful canter under the beating sun. I slid from his back to the ground and wrapped the reins securely around the trunk of a young sapling. Then I walked to a tree stump to sit down and cool off for a while.

I know I couldn't have had my back to Benny for more than a few seconds when a grunt I'd never heard before made me whirl around. I was aghast.

Benny was straining the reins to their limit, almost sitting on his haunches. The pull of his weight was tying the reins even tighter to the sapling, which made Ben pull still harder with another grunt. His strong back was finally too much for the old leather of the bridle: the cheek straps gave with a sharp snap. Benny recovered his balance, hesitated for only a second, and bounded off in a gallop right past me.

I shot out a hand to stop him and caught nothing but the rush of air. I was still staring incredulously as he leapt out of the woods, heading for the barn, the upper half of his bridle dangling around his ears.

"Benny! Benny!" I yelled. "Come back! Stop! Benny B-e-e-n-n-y-y-y!"

But he was gone, out of sight, although I could still hear his hoofbeats racing across the dry fields.

A short distance away, when I stopped to pick up the bit Benny had lost in the knee-high weeds, the blood rushed to my head and with it, a blinding anger.

The heat of the August afternoon was no match for the heat of my temper. I trekked furiously out of the woods into the intense sun, making my way back to the trail. As I strode closer to the house, the steel bit warm in my fist, the reins dragging in the dust, I had only one thought: how to get even with Benny.

As I marched along the driveway past the back porch, Mom stepped out and called, "Norma, what happened? I saw Benny go tearing by a while ago and was just about to go looking for you." The worry in her voice was plain.

"Benny broke his bridle when I tied him up. He ran home and left me *stranded* in the *woods!*" I called to her without stopping, and crossed the road to where Benny was standing, waiting for someone to open the gate so he could return to his walnut tree.

Instead I opened the barn door and hazed Benny into his big box stall, closing the lower half of the stall door after him. I leaned across the top of the closed door, raised my arm holding the bit and reins high in the air and brought the reins down with all my strength across Ben's back. There was a resounding crack of leather against his warm wet flesh.

Benny couldn't have been more startled: he shied from me to the other side of the stall, a confused look in his eyes which were now rolling with fear.

"That'll teach you to run off and leave me like that," I shrieked. The stall wasn't quite big enough for Benny to escape the second lash from the reins.

"I hate you! I *hate* you, Benny!"

The tears streamed down my face as I raised my arm to strike him for the third time. His dark eyes were wide and ringed with white. The reins had left dark wet stripes on his pinto coat.

Suddenly I was jerked away from the stall and swung around to face Mom. She grabbed my arms and shook me until my knees grew weak and I wanted to sink to the ground. Then she took me in her arms and waited for the river of tears to subside.

As I grew calmer, Mom said in a wonderfully soothing way, "Norma, Norma, Norma, Benny loves you. It was a nasty trick, yes, but that's one of the wiles of old Benny. You're still getting used to each other. He's trying you out a little, as Grandpa told you he would, and you can't whip him. You'll break his heart, Norma!"

She waited a minute and then said, "You know you don't really hate him. You know that, don't you?"

I stared at her for a moment, wondering how she could possibly know. Mom knew nothing about horses in general and very little more about Benny in particular. Maybe, I thought, she knows me.

I shuffled over to the water trough and leaned against the damp edge where I couldn't see Benny in his stall.

"I don't hate Benny, Mom. You're right. I really

do love him. I just lost my temper. I don't want to be cruel to him," I said between sniffles.

I knew, though, that for a few horrible moments I did mean to hurt him and it frightened me to have found out that I had a few bad traits myself.

"I'm sure, Norma, that old Ben will be very forgiving. Go try to make it up to him. Animals have an extra sense about them, sometimes more than we humans have."

Mom studied my face for a moment. Then she went out through the barnyard gate and across the road to the house without glancing back at me.

I turned to Benny's stall and was surprised to see that he had moved up to the half-door and thrust his head out. Determined to regain all the confidence and love I had probably lost, I ran back into the feed room, grabbed a rag and a handful of oats and rushed into Benny's stall.

It seemed unbelievable to me at the time but Benny's nostrils quivered with a welcome whinny as though nothing at all had happened. He stretched his nose eagerly forward for the oats and chewed them contentedly as I rubbed him down. I removed what was left of the broken bridle from his ears and slipped his halter back into place. Old Ben still showed no resentment.

I was so happy and grateful I started to cry. Then I

talked to him, trying to tell him how sorry I was, how it would never happen again, and marveled at the same time at the way he seemed to understand and at the depth of his feeling.

I turned him out into the barnyard and watched as he searched for the dustiest spot he could find to roll his sticky body. He rolled completely over not once or twice but three times, heaved himself to his feet, and with a satisfying shake made a thick cloud of dust all around him. Then he ambled slowly into the pasture to hunt for a succulent patch of clover.

Grandpa repaired the bridle for me that evening as I told him briefly about the afternoon's incident. I was too ashamed to admit to him what I had really done to Benny. Grandpa didn't question me but he somehow knew what happened.

The next day, Sunday, was another hot one and although school was starting on Monday, I disturbed Benny only long enough to curry and brush him and remove the burrs from his forelock and tail. We were friends again. And for the rest of that day my thoughts were a resolution that I would never again lose my temper with him and that we would always be friends. I had the feeling that I had been taught a lesson I would never completely forget.

THREE

Unwelcome Gifts

After school started, my daily rides were not so long as they had been. The days shortened and became cooler. Soon I could see my breath and Benny's on the crisp autumn air. Grandpa, with the help of Howdy and Earl, began preparing the barn for winter.

And Benny, with no help from anyone but nature, was also preparing for the cold Michigan weather: his fine pinto coat grew long and thick, giving his firm body a fat shaggy look. He no longer spent the whole day under the walnut tree.

The brisk air sparked the streak of mischief in him

as he frisked around. He would urge a steer into a race by nipping his flanks until the steer had no choice but to run. The wild pheasant found no peace in the high grasses of the pasture where Benny, like a hunting dog, would flush them out and watch their frightened flight, their bright feathers whirring against the deep indigo of the cold sky. A stray pig would very often be heard squealing his way back to a small hole in the fence, Benny in close pursuit yet always careful not to overtake the pig.

Or he would run races with himself or the wind, his long black tail almost straight up in the air and his short legs propelling him forward with astonishing speed. The landing of a pigeon on a fence post near him was an invitation to charge with a snort, frighten off the intruder, and go galloping and bucking again over the hills of the pasture.

He may have been an old horse in years, but his antics were those of a colt.

Autumn turned quickly into the cold sharp weather of November but as yet there was very little snow. Benny was now being stabled every night and although his furry coat was probably ample to keep him warm, he also had the extra protection of a deep blue stable blanket, his birthday present from me.

Since no one seemed to know Ben's exact birth date, and since January 1st, the automatic birthday of registered thoroughbreds, seemed too impersonal, I saw no reason why Benny's birthday shouldn't be the same as mine. That year—my eleventh birthday and Benny's nineteenth—my parents gave me a beautiful western saddle and a hand-woven Indian saddle blanket. Every weekend and many evenings thereafter Benny and I spent getting used to this fine saddle. Benny seemed to enjoy it as much as I did, once it was on. Getting it on, however, was another story.

But his new stable blanket, he merely tolerated. Even though it was a little large, the blanket looked grand on him but that didn't affect his feeling about it. Every winter evening as I put it on, I had to keep a sharp watch. When I reached under his stomach for the straps, his ears would fall back in warning and as I fastened the straps snugly to the hooks, he would swing his head around at me with his teeth bared. A slap on the nose never cured him either of flattening his ears or baring his teeth. And his feelings about the blanket never changed.

Every morning when I went to the barn before school to feed him and turn him out for exercise, his blanket looked comically like a pair of wrinkled pajamas. There were never any tears in it, so I knew he never grabbed it with his teeth to try to rip it off

during the night. Only the fastener on the chest kept it from slipping completely under his belly. Often I would find the back half of it in a mound covering only his shoulders and withers. When I tried to reprimand him, he assumed such an air of bland innocence that I could only laugh.

There was another battle with Benny every time I tightened the saddle girth. He looked absolutely ferocious and would swell his stomach so that I couldn't tighten the girth. I didn't catch on to his little trick, however, until the first time I led him out of the barn to mount. When I put my weight in the stirrup, the saddle slipped around to his side and I found myself flat on my back on the cold ground.

Grandpa, watching and laughing at my predicament, told me an easy solution: it was a way to fight Benny's little trick with one of my own.

"Horses," he said, "are famous for that. It's not natural for a horse to wear a saddle, so he finds a way to make it as comfortable as possible. You and I and even Benny knows that it certainly won't hurt him to have a tight girth around his belly as long as you fit it properly. We don't want him to get saddle sores, you know."

I had been listening to this sitting on the ground. Now Grandpa paused to give me a chance to get up. He patted Benny affectionately on his spotted side and pulled the saddle around and up to its proper position.

"Norma Jean, let me tell you a little something about the innards of this old animal. It's a fact that he bloats himself on purpose. But you've got an advantage over him. You know what he's going to do. The thing is, he doesn't know what *you're* going to do."

He took another chew on his tobacco.

"Horses," he continued, "automatically *un*bloat themselves when they walk. That's when the girth gets loose again. Know what I'm gettin' at?"

"Oh, I see, Grandpa, I see what you mean. I put the saddle on, tighten the girth a little, then walk him out and when he doesn't expect anything, finish tightening it."

"That's the idea. Pretty soon it won't be any problem at all. Go see how it works."

I led Ben forward a few steps, reached under him and quickly slipped the girth strap into a firm position. I smiled and nodded at Grandpa as I mounted Benny, successfully this time, and jogged off for a short ride, smug in the knowledge that I had put one over on foxy Benny.

FOUR

Snowbound

U. S. 1333465

Winter in central Michigan is dedicated to winter sports. The first snowfall was the signal to haul toboggans and sleds out of summer storage and prepare for some brilliant snowy weekends. Skates were dragged out of the attic, the blades honed and the leather polished by my brothers for some flashy skating on frozen ponds or the skating rink at high school. Neighborhood hockey games were scheduled and skiing equipment was cleaned and waxed for the shimmering slopes.

Snow tires replaced those with smaller treads on farmers' tractors and on nearly all cars; tire chains were thrown into trunks for emergencies. Bags of salt were in handy places for slippery sidewalks. Snowplows and sand trucks were put to work on the county roads and snow shovels became as familiar a sight on sidewalks and paths as a broom in the kitchen.

Our winter clothes were so heavy and we wore so many of them that often only our eyes could be seen as they peered out from layers of warm mufflers, hats and earmuffs.

Benny was outfitted with ice calks on his shoes, metal pieces tapered downward to a point to prevent his slipping on icy surfaces. These calks meant that Benny and I could enjoy winter riding with a minimum of danger to either of us. I often thought, though, how painful it would be if Benny accidentally stomped those sharp ice calks into my foot.

Christmas had always been the happiest time of the year for me, and after Benny became a member of the family my favorite holiday was more exciting than ever. Grandpa and I would spend hours in the barn just before Christmas, putting a festive touch here and there. We tied Christmas ribbons on Benny's halter and adorned his stall with a wreath of pine boughs, pine cones, and holly, set off with a big red bow.

The stall floor was always kept meticulously clean. For Christmas we covered it with a couple of extra armloads of fresh sweet straw, so that Benny was wading in it up to his knees. His oats were flavored with a handful of wheat, which Benny loved, but was never allowed at any other time of the year. Too much wheat could make a horse seriously ill, or even kill him, and so I measured it out very sparingly, no matter how he begged. To make up for that I searched the hay mow for forkfuls of hay with a little extra timothy which he liked almost as well as wheat.

And Benny seemed to catch the spirit of Christmas. His welcoming whinnies each time I entered the barn were cheerier. He nudged me with his nose more often, as if he were seeking some clue to his gift from me. I rewarded him only with a carrot or a lump of sugar. I was keeping his gift a secret until Christmas morning.

A continuing light snowfall increased our Christmasy feelings. Mom put beautiful greens and holly on the fireplace mantel. In the evenings, the flickering red and yellow flames of the fire threw the shadows of the decorations against the high white ceiling. Mistletoe hung from door lintels and a sprig of pine and holly was attached to the pull-down lamp over the long dining-room table.

The house was filled with the fragrance of pine and the spicy aroma of cookies baking. Homemade fudge, golden tangerines and nuts tempted everyone who passed the bowls that held them.

For eleven months and two weeks of the year, most of our party-giving, relaxing and living was done in the recreation room with its comfortable furniture, braided rugs that could be rolled back for dancing, and pine-paneled walls. The holiday celebrations and entertaining were always in the living room where the big brick fireplace welcomed us with its warmth, where the trimmed and lighted tree added color to the room's charm.

As Christmas came closer our enthusiasm mounted. Pop came home from his office almost every night with mysterious packages which he promptly hid, and so added to our excitement. Even our grandmother, Susie (we never called her anything but Susie), would come over every day to help with cooking and baking and other special preparations.

School vacation during the Christmas holidays meant that Howdy and Earl were able to spend more time enjoying winter sports and I was able to spend more time with Benny. Even Grandpa was glad to have us home for these two weeks because Earl and Howdy and I could give him a real hand with the chores, always more difficult when the animals had to be kept inside.

Christmas Day, when it came at last, was an exciting climax. Earl, Howdy and I were up before dawn on that morning. Mom and Pop were not allowed to sleep much later than five-thirty and even relatives and friends who were spending Christmas with us were hustled out of bed before the sun came up.

Susie and Grandpa were always awake and about early anyway. But one of us would make a quick phone call to them as soon as we were out of bed. They'd arrive carrying a large straw clothes basket between them, laden with gifts. With their free hands, they brushed snowflakes from their heads and shoulders.

"Ain't any better way to have a Christmas morning than with a light snowfall outside," Susie said.

"Oh, there ain't, ain't there?" Earl said, teasing her for the millionth time about using *ain't*.

Susie laughed and shook her head at Earl, refusing

to acknowledge that *ain't* wasn't acceptable English today as it had been when she went to school. "Styles change," she'd say, "even in grammar."

There was confusion and glee in equal parts as we opened our presents and ate a chaotic breakfast. Then Grandpa, Pop and I bundled up in our warm coats and made our way across to the barn for the morning chores and the presentation of my gift to Ben.

Benny disliked the noise of rustling paper, so I had not wrapped his new handstitched leather halter. But I had tied a bright red ribbon on it. Benny whinnied a welcome to us before we could get the barn door open. He sniffed at his new halter almost disinterestedly as we shouted Merry Christmas and laughed at his sophistication. He was much more interested in getting his breakfast and nudged me often to show his impatience.

Vacations and holidays always seemed to speed by more swiftly than routine days, so it wasn't long before New Year's had come and gone and we settled back into the normal winter schedule.

Then the blizzard came.

The snow fell and fell and fell for several days and nights until the roads were impassable, schools and businesses closed, and power lines were whipped down by the shrieking wind. Drifts built rapidly into small white mountains, covering fences and automobiles. No one left the safety of his house unless absolutely necessary.

With the electric stove and the furnace out of commission, the fireplace in the living room was our only source of heat and was also the place where all the cooking had to be done. Mom tacked blankets up on the two doorways into the living room to keep the heat in.

At first it was fun, almost like another holiday. I didn't have to go to school, and living by candlelight made the evenings cozier and longer. We lived as the settlers in the old West must have lived. All our water for washing and cooking had to be heated in the fireplace. Repairs were impossible to make on the power lines. Even the county road commission could not free its snow equipment from the deep drifts.

But as the blizzard continued, I discovered that there could be no riding at all and much of my waking time had to be spent in front of the fire.

The front yard in a blizzard was a good playground for burning off some energy. Despite biting wind and flying snow, we ran races around the maple trees. We tried making snowmen but the air was too cold and the snow too dry for good packing. We played "Fox and Geese," tramping out a large circle in the snow and cutting paths in it like a pie. One of us was the fox; the other two, the geese. Home, where you were safe, was at the very center of the circle and you had to stay on the lines. Whichever goose the fox caught was "it" and became the fox. We couldn't play for long at a time because it was so freezing cold but we did exhaust ourselves and sharpen our appetites.

And still the blizzard went on. I noticed that Mom and Pop began exchanging glances at meal times. If the storm kept up, we'd soon run out of food. And when the storm did let up, it would be days before the county could get its equipment freed and the roads cleared.

And then I had my idea. Why couldn't Benny and I do it? Parker's grocery was only about a mile and a half away. Surely I could strap a few necessities to the back of my saddle.

"NO!" Mom and Pop said simultaneously.

"But I know the way. Cars can't get through and it's too far to walk in this weather. But, gosh, Benny and I can go where cars and people can't."

"It's out of the question. It's too dangerous." Pop pulled his blanket more tightly around his shoulders as he sat before the fire. "That's asking a little too much of Benny, Norma Jean. He's too old for that kind of riding. And this weather is too bad, even for you."

Earl and Howdy were surprisingly quiet. They let me know, though, that they thought I was crazy:

who'd want to go out in weather like this and ride horseback except a lunatic!

But Mom had other ideas. "Howard," she said to Pop, "maybe one of the *boys* could ride Benny up to Parker's. We are getting low on food and neither of us could attempt such a trip."

"Gee, do we really need food *that* badly?" Howdy asked.

"Howdy's just the guy for the job," Earl said.

"Not me, Earl. You. You're the hero in the family."

"But you're the star, Howd. You should be the one to bring home the bacon."

"All right, boys, calm down," Pop said. They were laughing but I was serious.

"Well, it's too late today to worry about it. Let's wait and see how the weather is tomorrow. Maybe the wind will let up a little. Who knows, it might even stop snowing," Mom said.

I was disappointed and sulked. I *knew* Benny and I could do it.

Earl and Howdy, once started, kept up their banter and even I, in spite of the sulks, finally had to laugh and join in. It was hard to stay in a sour mood when the rest of the family was in such a good humor. The warmth of the fire made us forget the gloom and the merciless cold outside.

As soon as I awoke the next morning, before I had looked out the window, I knew there was a change in the weather. No wind whistling through the shingles, and it wasn't snowing either. There'd be no trouble at all getting to Parker's grocery. Even if Mom and Pop wouldn't let me ride that far, at least Benny and I would be able to get out for a short ride.

"Good morning, dear," Mother said when I went in to breakfast. "Going to ride Benny up to Parker's today?"

"Mom! You mean I *can?*"

"I don't know why not. The weather seems to be clearing a little. It'll still be a few days before the plows can get through. And knowing you, you'll be out there riding Benny anyway."

Mom held the grill over the fresh morning fire, toasting bread for breakfast. Pop took hold of the handle of the bubbling coffee pot and removed it from the hook over the flames. Good smelling steam came from the spout as he poured the coffee into his cup.

"There'll be no keeping you off that horse, no matter what," Pop said, "and now since I won't worry that you and Benny might freeze to death, why go ahead and ride to Parker's." He winced a little as the hot coffee touched his lips.

"It's a good thing Benny has calks on his shoes, so he can't go down on ice," Pop went on. "You just be careful, though, of deep drifts. And don't let the snow get balled up in his hoofs. Take something to scrape it out with."

"Oh, I'll be careful. And Benny will know what drifts to avoid. I've been dying to go for a ride and it will be more fun to have a purpose. We're going to save the Cline family from starvation!"

"Bow to Norma, Girl Wonder! She's going to save us from starvation," Howdy mimicked.

"The Pony Express rides again! Or is she the Lone Ranger in disguise? No, that's Danny Boone rushing to the fort to bring help from the Indians!" Earl galloped around the living room, slapping his imaginary horse on the flanks.

"You're both too chicken to do it," I snapped back at them. "I guess you know now who the important member of this family is!"

The fun continued all through breakfast. Then I dressed warmly for the ride. Earl and Howdy, still yelling ridiculous taunts at me, nearly threw me out the front door into the snow.

"If you're not back in three weeks, we'll send out a search party!"

"Watch out for frostbite. We may have to cut off your nose when you get back!"

I quickly scooped up a handful of snow and hurled

it at the front door. It fell at their feet and they ducked into the house, slamming the door after them.

The sky was still overcast with dark clouds; the temperature had dropped a little more. Every breath of sharp air stung my nostrils. I laughed to myself, wondering how I would look with a frostbitten nose.

The expanse of trackless white between the house and barn made it look as though Cook Road did not exist. Last night's boot tracks to and from the barn were completely covered. The mailbox seemed to sit on top of the snow, not on a post. I raised the red flag on the side of the mailbox, the usual signal for the mailman to stop to pick up mail in case he had nothing to deliver. How silly I am, I thought! He'll never make it today!

Benny welcomed me with his usual loud whinny, which steamed up the cold air. I removed his disheveled blanket and let him out of his stall. He jogged eagerly outside to the water trough to drink thirstily through a freshly chopped hole in the thick ice. Then, with nose to the ground like a hunting dog, he searched for a soft mattress of snow to roll in.

While he rolled, I cleaned his stall and put a small amount of oats in his feed box. He finally sauntered in and while he was eating, I brushed his thick coat and got the bridle, saddle and blanket ready for our ride.

As I worked, in my mind I went over the route to Parker's grocery: You go east on Cook Road, turn left on Embury, right on Grand Blanc about a mile later, then up the hill and there you are. No traffic to worry about today!

Benny was well protected by his winter coat, and the cold air was stimulating to him. He moved forward easily in the powdery snow. Just before we reached Embury Road, we met our first deep snowdrift.

"Well, Benny, old friend," I said, "this should be no problem to an old snowplow like you. What do you say? Shall we go right through it or shall we try to go around? It doesn't look too deep. Let's go through it."

Benny slowed to a walk. First he sank one round furry leg cautiously into the snow and then another. His ears were perked forward and his head was slightly lowered. He was clearly enjoying himself. He brought one leg high out of the snow for the next step. In no time he was out of the drift and back in his jog again.

"If they're all like this, Benny boy, we won't have any problem at all." Ben paid no attention to my rewarding pat.

As we turned onto Embury Road, I could see that the rest of the ride wouldn't be quite so easy. Looking down the first hill and up the next as far as Susie and Grandpa's, Embury Road looked like a beach on Lake Huron, with sand dunes burying the road and the fences alongside it. This worried me. There would be no going around those snowdrifts, not with buried fences on both sides.

"Well, shall we go on, Benny? No sense even thinking about it: Howdy and Earl would laugh us out of the house if we went back now."

The grey clouds hadn't lifted and a slight wind had sprung up, blowing snow across the tops of the drifts. The trail we made in the snow would soon be covered, I thought. It's a good thing I know where I'm going.

We crept down the Embury Road hill. Ben picked the way. I was merely a passenger along for the ride. I let Benny figure out which drifts to avoid and which he could plow through; I knew his instincts were sharper than mine. But I kept a firm knee grip on him in case he went down or decided, as he did once or twice, to leap through a drift. I had no desire to be dumped into a bank of cold snow.

The wind snapped at my nose and at Benny's thick coat. It rattled the snakelike branches of the trees; the big ones creaked before it. The smoke from Grandpa and Susie's chimney in the distance was swept up into the air in spurts. Benny gave no thought to the wind nor much to me. His body was still warm, his eyes alert, and his neck bowed as he made his way through each snowbank.

Grandpa and Susie waved to us from a living-room window as we passed their gate. Benny picked up his jog again on a level clear stretch, protected from the wind on both sides by woods. We stopped just the other side of the woods, before tackling more snow-drifts, and Benny waited patiently as I scraped a ball of packed snow from each hoof.

After a few more minor skirmishes, we reached the crest of the last hill on Embury Road. I pulled Ben up to survey the hill on Grand Blanc Road to Parker's. Benny, who never wanted to stand still, also seemed to be making his own calculations on the best tactic for getting through what looked to be the deepest drifts yet.

We walked slowly down to the corner of Embury and Grand Blanc. Then Benny lowered his head, his nose almost touching the snow as though it could tell him how deep the drift was, and plunged without hesitation into the white bank. His furry legs sank and sank. Benny lunged but his hooves found only a deeper pocket. He struggled but the snow wedged his legs so firmly that his stomach rested on top of the snow. *His* legs were completely invisible but mine, feet in stirrups, were stretched out full length on both sides of him. We were a comical sight, I knew, as I wondered what on earth to do next.

"Easy, Benny. Take it easy," I said. "Don't move. I don't want you to break a leg trying to get out of this." I kept telling Benny to relax as I slipped cautiously from the saddle.

My feet and legs disappeared immediately into the loose snow but only up to my knees. Benny's weight along with mine had sunk him deeper into the snow. I pushed ahead and found the drift growing shallow about five feet ahead. Benny watched me intently, his ears forward.

As I made my way back through my own tracks, Benny whinnied to me as he always did to help resolve my doubts or give me encouragement. Then I began digging with my mittened hands, scooping out two trenches in front of Ben's forelegs.

"If my hands don't freeze off, Benny, I'll have you out in no time. Just don't try to jump out—yet."

I worked frantically, afraid Benny would get impatient, struggle some more, and get himself more firmly stuck than ever. The snow soaked through my mittens and packed into my boots. My scarf fell from around my ears and the wind lashed my hair into my face. Benny's mane waved as the loose snow sifted lightly over his long black tail outspread on top of the drift.

Slowly, slowly, the snow piled up in little mounds as I scooped harder, racing the wind which was trying to refill every ditch I made. Finally, I had scooped his forelegs clear, so that he'd be able to touch ground with his calks if he and I could free his hind legs from their white trap.

I told Ben to give it a try. He gave a violent lurch, his neck stretched as far forward as it would go. Then he gave a loud grunt and still another lurch and grunt and he was standing in snow to his knees, shaking himself as though he'd just had a roll in the mud.

"Benny, you're out! Easy now, Ben. Don't go off without me."

I gathered up the reins and managed to pull my cold stiff body into the saddle. Benny trudged wearily up the rest of the hill into the driveway of Parker's grocery.

After Benny was rested and given a little water to drink and I was warm, I lashed the food to my saddle and started back on the long road home. The grey clouds, skimming overhead, seemed lower and heavier than on the trip over but no snow came from them.

The wind, however, would keep us company as long as we were going to be out in it. It was as strong as ever. We went slowly downhill to the treacherous snowbank. I knew it would be madness to try to go through it again but I was unsure of the snow's depth on either edge of the road.

I left it to Benny who lowered his head again, like a divining rod, searching out the easiest route. But I didn't leave it entirely to him. I realized now that Benny needed my help. He could easily break a leg by being trapped above his hocks or knees where he had no firm footing underneath. I kept him at a slow walk and bent to the side to see how far his shaggy legs sank into the snow at each step.

The wind hadn't quite covered all evidence of our recent struggle, so we both knew exactly which spots to avoid. We skirted the drift along one edge of the road. My back soon began to ache from bending over but I didn't dare stop until we were safely through.

Eager to slip back into his jog, now that he was heading for home, Benny became impatient with the slow pace I held him to and worked himself into a slight sweat. I was tired and getting very cold, so the last half mile seemed interminable. When at last we saw our farm in the distance, it had never looked so beautiful to me, ever.

FIVE

Three's a Crowd

In the spring, nature began removing patches of Benny's winter coat by the handful. Wherever he went he left a trace of himself. Bunches of spotted hair were on tree trunks where he rubbed his neck or on the ground where he rolled. It clung to the saddle pad and girth, so that both had to be shaken and brushed after each use. I was covered with his hair after a ride or after currying and brushing him. Yet for several weeks, in spite of the constant shedding, he looked as roly-poly as ever.

It wasn't until the blossoms were on the apple trees and the wild violets sprouted in the woods that his slick new short hair eventually pushed off the last of his winter coat. His legs were slim again; his barrel, sleek.

Spring is the time for romance and Benny fell in love.

He fell in love with Golden Arrow who became a member of the Cline family when her owner lost interest in riding. She was pure white and her eyes were a soft deep brown. The tip of her tail just touched the ground and her silvery mane flowed along her neck. Her Tennessee Walker breeding gave her dignity and style. She towered above Benny by a good two hands and was nearly ten years his junior.

But Benny asserted his seniority and masculinity at once, disproving the belief that mares are usually dominant over geldings.

After letting them stare at each other over distant fences for a few days, Grandpa and I watched nervously as we turned Goldie into the pasture with Benny. They rubbed noses instantly, their shapely ears pointed at each other, twitching slightly. They arched their necks and lowered their heads slowly toward the ground, noses still touching. Simultaneously, they squealed. Goldie swung around in a flash and kicked out with both hind legs.

Benny dodged easily. His ears dropped back flat against his head in anger, his eyes darkened. He leaped forward before Goldie could get her hind legs off the ground for another kick and bit her smartly on the flank. He pushed against her, nipping her again and again. He was too close for Goldie to get any power behind her sharp hooves. Goldie broke forward into a wild gallop, trying to get far enough ahead to give her hind legs room for a solid kick into Benny's chest or ribs.

"We've got to stop them, Grandpa. They're fighting! Benny's too old to fight. She'll hurt him! She'll kill him!"

I ran to the pasture gate, shrieking at Benny and Goldie to stop. It was too late. Words were useless. Benny and Goldie were fighting for leadership. They grunted and squealed as an occasional kick caught Benny in the chest or as Benny's teeth sank into Goldie's flank.

"There's nothing we can do now, Norma," Grandpa

said as he joined me at the gate. "We can't go in there. They'd either run away from us or fight right over the top of us. Leastways, we just have to stay out of their way and keep hoping."

Grandpa was chewing excitedly and I could see that he was as worried as I was.

Their savage chase brought them around in a semi-circle so that they were once again heading our way. Benny was still thrusting his bared teeth at Goldie's silver flanks and Goldie still fought to catch Benny with just the right kick. As they approached the gate, Goldie suddenly changed her tactics and whirled around to catch Benny's neck in her teeth. But at that instant, as though Benny had read her mind, he swung around the other way and whipped his short hind legs into her barrel. I could hear the wheeze of air through her lungs.

Goldie was stunned by Benny's maneuver. She brought herself to a dead stop, head lowered, her breath coming in heavy gasps. Benny watched her suspiciously, trying to anticipate her next move. With her body now relaxed from exhaustion, Goldie looked like a tired grey farm horse, the sweat showing the black skin under her white coat.

It was Benny who made the next move. He walked warily to her. Again their noses touched. Grandpa and I held our breath, wondering if it was going to start all over again. Both horses squealed but their ears remained forward. Goldie pawed the ground defiantly but Benny's eyes flashed a warning. He then walked nonchalantly to the shade of the walnut tree and stuck his nose in the cold water. Goldie remained where she was for a moment, then followed him slowly and stuck her nose in the cool water, imitating Benny. Goldie had accepted Benny as leader.

From then on, Benny and Goldie were inseparable. And as summer came, bringing mosquitoes and flies, they put their new companionship to practical use. On very hot days when the insects were particularly bothersome, Goldie and Benny would stand head to

tail under the walnut tree. Benny's black tail would whip across Goldie's chest, shooing away flies while Goldie's dusty white tail flicked them away from Benny's forequarters.

Benny was boss, dictator and ruler of his domain. No doubt about it. When Benny moved out to graze,

Goldie followed submissively, accepting every move Benny made without question. Goldie sometimes kicked out with her heels if Benny happened to nip her playfully but there was no malice in her.

Goldie was a pleasure to ride. Her gaits were smooth, especially her Tennessee Walk which she could maintain at a good speed for quite a distance. But she didn't have either the spirit or the enthusiasm of Benny.

When Goldie first arrived, Earl and Howdy were quite willing to ride with me but as they got busier with farmwork and schoolwork and sports, they had less and less time for riding and horses. Earl, now a senior in high school, was determined to get good grades. He hoped to take pre-law courses at the University of Michigan. He would spend the summer doing road work for the Genesee County Road Commission.

Howdy, on the other hand, would help Grandpa mow and rake hay, thresh wheat and oats, bale hay and wheat straw (oat straw was plowed under because the animals were much more likely to eat it than the wheat straw). Howdy's farm labors were not so back-breaking as they sounded. At harvest time, for instance, several of his friends were hired to help and they made light work of the most tedious jobs.

And he had expert direction and help, besides,

from Grandpa and a "hand" for spring and fall plowing, cultivating, planting and seeding, corn threshing and grinding, mechanical maintenance of the machinery, care of the animals. But he did a lot and toughened up his muscles long before football practice started.

Mom always felt safe around horses "as long as I keep my two feet on the ground," she said. She never became a rider. She wouldn't so much as sit on Goldie.

But not Pop. He learned to ride and loved it. And that's why Sunday mornings became very important to me.

Before breakfast, just as the sun showed over the horizon, Pop and I would be saddling Benny and Goldie. We alternated horses every Sunday. We'd tramp out deep green paths in the fields as Benny and Goldie cantered through the dew-topped grass. The sky was brilliant those early Sundays and lightened slowly from the east. Benny and Goldie were full of spirit, and very frisky in the cool dawn air.

Pop was a little unsure of himself as a horseman at first and though he never became expert, he was skillful enough to feel comfortable in the saddle, which was all that mattered to either of us. And if his interest in horses never matched mine, he shared my enthusiasm and encouraged it by granting every reasonable request that I made.

I might say right now that he did the same for Earl and Howdy, which explains, I guess, how an eagerness to please him was generated in all three of us. His respect for us and our different temperaments helped us respect each other in spite of faults, disagreements and occasional arguments, and it was one of the reasons, I think, that we developed a staunch loyalty to him and to one another.

Benny knew that Pop was a part-time rider. But he also knew that Pop was a man to be respected and obeyed. He never took advantage of Pop's mistakes and seemed as intent as we were on enjoying the freshness of the morning, the early songs of the birds and all the soft sounds of the waking day. And, of course, Ben communicated his enjoyment to Goldie.

That summer I learned about the changing boundaries and the history of our farm from Pop. Sitting astride Benny or Goldie, talking about a place he loved, gave Pop the exercise, air and relaxation which he couldn't get working in his law office six days a week. This way, too, he was able to keep a watchful and proud eye on the growing crops, check the condition of the fences, the pasture and the orchards. But best of all, we shared and enjoyed each other's company.

At the end of our ride as we passed the house on our way to the barn, we'd get the marvelous breakfast smells from the kitchen—bacon or sausage frying, coffee brewing. And we knew the pancake batter was ready for the hot griddle. We'd put Benny and Goldie out to pasture, hang up our riding gear as fast as possible, and race each other to the sunny kitchen to eat.

On summer weekdays my explorations of the countryside went beyond the boundaries of the farm. I discovered to my delight that within a radius of a few miles there were several people, some of them my own age, who owned horses and rode as often as I did. Amy Bentley, Lorrie Davis and I became special friends and spent many afternoons making up posses and chasing outlaws. We three and others who joined us took turns playing the "bad guys" and the "good guys." It was childish, but fun. Lorrie didn't have a horse of his own and so he rode Goldie most of the time.

The game, "Red Rover, Come Over," on horseback, was one of our favorites but very strenuous, particularly for the horses, and could be played only on days that were not too hot. One horse and rider were "it" and stood in the center of an imaginary circle. The rest of us, usually from three to eight horses, lined up neck and neck some distance away. "It" yelled, "Rover, Red Rover, come over, come over," and the rest of us heeled our mounts into a racing gallop.

The object was to tear past "it" without being touched either by him or his horse, to the safety zone on the opposite side of the circle. Those who were caught also became "it" and took their places in the center. After two or three wild rushes across the

circle, the "its" outnumbered those still free until sometimes only one rider remained uncaught.

By the end of the game, the horses were flecked with sweat and lather; the riders, exhausted. Our throats were dry from yelling good-natured insults or encouragement. The ground was thoroughly torn up, which is why we were always careful to choose a field where there were no crops.

There were occasional spills. Sometimes a rider was thrown when two horses collided. But miraculously, neither horse nor rider was ever injured.

Benny was a marvel at dodging the "its." His speed, sudden turns, and instantaneous stops were like those of a polo pony and he almost always brought me out the winner.

Goldie, though light on her feet, preferred to race straight ahead and almost never could avoid being caught. I never knew whether it was reflexes, training, or temperament, but she was no horse for this game.

Lorrie, a boy on a farm near ours and a fine rider, gave her every help, and he himself played the game with his whole heart. Perhaps it was just that Goldie would not compete with her beloved Benny. For adore him she did, completely—until The King came along.

SIX

Reckless Rider

The King was owned by Amy Bentley and was the
third horse of our trio. He was not a purebred
but very handsome nonetheless. He showed strong
traces of· Morgan blood: the heavy neck, gracefully
arched. He was a bay with a glistening coat and his
long face was accented by a bold white blaze which
came to a point at his upper lip. His eyes, though big,
seemed to have no real depth. He was solidly built but
slender and treated Benny with disdain.

I remember the afternoon it first became apparent.
As on every other afternoon our talk got around to the
qualities of the horses we were riding.

Lorrie was saying, "Even if Goldie doesn't belong to me, she's got the best color and is the prettiest."

"But you've got to admit, even if Benny is a mixed breed, he's very smart."

Amy smiled and said, "Well, I'll admit what you say about Benny and Goldie but you'll have to admit that The King has fire. After all, he's part Morgan."

Just then The King pulled his nose down to chase away a fly buzzing around his knees and he even showed his spirit when he chased flies. Amy smiled and tossed her long brown hair, almost the color of The King's, as we kept the horses to a slow walk, three abreast, along Cook Road.

"Just because they aren't part Morgan doesn't make either Goldie or Benny any less good, Amy," I said. "Sure, The King's spirited, and smart too, but I'll bet anything he won't live as long as Benny has already and if he does, that he won't have as much pep."

That ought to silence her and take her down a peg, I thought.

Lorrie laughed. "No matter what you say, Goldie's the nicest. Look how I have to keep her between Benny and The King because they keep giving each other dirty looks and would do worse if Goldie didn't keep them apart."

"I do think Benny's a little jealous of The King, Norma, don't you?" Amy asked.

She nudged The King into a canter, but her remark irked me just enough that I didn't follow suit. Lorrie, I could tell, was getting a little nervous. He didn't want to be caught in any silly girls' argument. When Amy saw that we weren't cantering after her, she pulled up and waved to us to catch up. Goldie trotted out and Benny immediately followed.

"Benny's not really jealous, do you think, Lorrie?" I gave Lorrie no time to answer the question but went on, "He's just sort of watching over his property. After all, he's been boss over Goldie for quite a while and Goldie hasn't been complaining. Has she, Lorrie?"

I said this when we were all three together again. Neither Amy nor I expected Lorrie to answer that question and he didn't. He wasn't sure whether we were kidding or whether this was going to end in a fight.

We walked on down the dusty road in silence, and I watched the shadows of the leaves dapple the horses. The afternoon was comfortably warm but not a day for chasing thieves or Indians. Then we reached a corner. As we turned, The King tried to crowd Benny but Benny moved fast and kept Goldie between himself and The King.

Goldie was enjoying the rivalry of the two jealous horses. She flirted with them by turns, ignoring first one and then the other.

"Well," I remarked after watching this performance, "Benny may be guarding his property but we know now that he won't pick a fight with The King over Goldie. And you'll have to admit that The King does try to goad him into it—sometimes."

I wondered what answer Amy would make to that.

"The King would never—ever—pick a fight with Benny, Norma, because there isn't anything to fight about. And besides, Benny's so much *smaller* and *older*, that even if they *did* fight, you know who'd win!"

"Hey c'mon, you girls," Lorrie broke in. "Knock it off. Let's talk about something else. So what if they're jealous. Just watch Goldie. She's no angel. She eggs them on and you both know it. And anyhow, it's a stupid argument. You know they won't fight, jealous or not, because we've already turned them out to pasture together plenty of times and they haven't so far. What makes you think they would now? I say it's a little good-natured competition."

Amy and I were a little ashamed of ourselves and tried to smile. Lorrie was right: it was senseless to talk that way and spoil our fun.

"Let's canter a little way and get some life into this party." Lorrie acted on his suggestion and without a signal from us, Benny and The King were off after Goldie.

The rush of air was cool on our foreheads. We

rode three abreast down the shadows, lengthening now in the late afternoon. To ride one behind another would be making a race of it and would put the two in back in danger of flying gravel.

We moved easily together in a smooth cadence. Benny's canter was effortless despite his short legs and he had no trouble keeping up with The King and Goldie. Amy, Lorrie and I didn't talk but simultaneously nodded at each other and urged the horses into a slow gallop. We were heading for an alfalfa field, long and level, where we'd let the horses enjoy a last run before slowing them to their cooling-off walk and the end of the ride.

I kept a close rein on Benny, for I knew that just the slightest encouragement would spark him into a burst of speed. He loved running only a little less than he loved racing. When there was competition around, he was eager to test it and the speed of his own fast legs.

Without warning, Amy yelled, "Let's race to the end of the field!"

Lorrie glanced at me, ready to accept the challenge.

"We'd better not," I answered. "It's not that far and once they get going they'll be hard to stop."

"What's the matter, Norma? Afraid The King will beat Benny?" Amy asked. She smiled and waited for me to reply. I shook my head but I didn't press Benny to run faster.

Suddenly Amy kicked her heels into The King's sides. His big bay body lunged forward, eager for the run. Before Lorrie could shorten his reins, Goldie leaped after The King. I quickly pulled back on my reins, keeping Benny to a slow gallop. Benny fought me hard as The King and Goldie pulled away. He wanted to whiz past them both. He especially wanted The King behind him.

Amy would think I was afraid to race her. But it wouldn't be a fair race, really. We'd been riding a long time and the horses were beginning to tire. I'll let it go this time, I thought, but another time I'll show her a thing or two.

As I watched, The King began pulling farther away from Goldie. Lorrie was managing to slow Goldie down but Amy, still hunched over The King's black mane like a jockey, was flailing his sides with her heels, urging him to his greatest speed. She'd better start slowing him soon, I thought, before she reaches the fence at the end of the field, unless she plans to gallop all the way home.

Benny and I caught up with Lorrie and we kept the horses to a panting trot. I glanced ahead to the gate at the end of the field. When I saw it was closed, I almost panicked. There wasn't time now for Amy to get The King safely stopped. That crazy horse, I thought, is either going to plow right through the barbed wire fence or try to jump it. Amy was a reckless rider but she wasn't expert enough for that kind of jump.

"Lorrie," I shouted. "The gate's closed. We've got to get to them." Lorrie looked toward the gate and swallowed hard.

My heels dug into Benny's sides as I thrust my hand forward and leaned over his neck. Benny leapt into his gallop. At last I had let him run. His short legs gathered speed as his body seemed to lower several inches nearer the ground. His ears were forward, watching The King and Amy gallop at a mad clip.

I could hear Goldie's hoofbeats behind us and knew that Lorrie had her running as fast as she could go.

Along with my fear for Amy and The King, I felt pride sweeping through me as we pulled farther and farther ahead of Lorrie and Goldie. Benny's full attention was now focused on The King. I could see that Amy was sawing on the reins, trying to bring The King back under control. She was fearfully aware of the closed gate and wire fence. The blindly racing King had his nose thrust forward as far as it would go and his ears pressed back against his neck, as though he were ready for a do-or-die battle with that fence.

"Benny!" I whispered into his ear. "Go, go, go. We've got to catch up with them!"

I pressed my hand encouragingly against Benny's sweaty neck. He answered with a flick of his ear. I pressed my legs tighter against his hot sides. His body lowered a trifle more and I felt him force himself into an even faster run. I was exhilarated and afraid. Benny's mane lashed my cheek but I could feel no smart. I was riding the wind—smooth, hot, and fast. The gap was closing slowly between The King and Benny but Amy and The King were moving rapidly nearer the fence.

Not entirely sure of what I was going to do if we caught up with them in time, I kept leaning over Benny's neck, whispering to him, hoping for a miracle that would slow The King down.

Benny's nose was now inches from The King's hind-quarters. The heavy wire fence loomed high ahead. Amy glanced over her shoulder at me. She had given up any hope of stopping The King and was trying to brace herself for the inevitable crash into the fence. The King's reins were flying in the wind and Amy had a fierce grip on the saddle horn. Her face was white and she was crying.

Somehow, the thought that Benny and I might charge through the barbed wire fence at breakneck speed, cutting and slicing ourselves, never entered my mind. My hand was still on Ben's neck but now it was I who was receiving encouragement, who was being urged to go on.

Suddenly, Benny lowered his head and summoned up one last burst of speed. It brought him shoulder to shoulder with The King and I felt my right leg being pushed against The King just in front of Amy's left leg. Benny was trying to push him around!

Amy was screaming. It would be useless to try to tell her what to do. I leaned to the right, trying to help Benny all I could. The King opened his mouth and grabbed for Benny just above the eye. But Benny deftly dodged him and pushed harder. I leaned my weight more, until I was almost over The King's neck.

The fence was right there before us, its steel barbs

glinting in the sun! Benny grunted and again we pushed The King. This time it worked. The King gave way and swerved sharply to the right. Amy lost her balance and fell against me. I heard the creak of the wire fence as Benny's left shoulder scraped against it at the same moment that I felt the leg of my blue jeans being ripped. I pushed hard against Amy, hoping to help her get upright in her saddle again.

Now Lorrie reached us and moved Goldie in from the other side against The King, hemming The King in so that he couldn't swing around to kick Benny. The King's eyes were wide with fright. Saliva dripped from his open mouth as he continued to make passes at Benny's head. Benny's ears were still flat against his neck and he bared his teeth angrily at The King.

Lorrie and I each managed to grab one of The King's wildly whipping reins. We kept Goldie and Benny pressed in close until exhaustion and the savage jerks we gave his mouth slowed him down. Little drops of blood dripped from his lips around the bit. We had had to curb him hard.

All three horses were wheezing noisily now. Lather and sweat from their shoulders and necks flew into our faces. The King dropped to a trot at last and we were able to bring him to a complete stop. He made no further move to kick or bite Benny. The three horses stood breathing hard, sides heaving, and let their heads hang wearily as they tried to regain their wind.

Amy was almost hysterical. She cried into The King's mane, her shoulders jerking convulsively. Lorrie slid from Goldie's back to the ground and tied Goldie's reins and The King's to the heavy wire fence.

For the first time, I thought of Benny's shoulder. Glancing down, I saw dark red blood making little rivers in the sweat and dirt on his leg. There was raw flesh where a large patch of his spotted hair was missing.

My own leg was throbbing with pain and I saw my blood slowly cover my shoe and drip to the ground. I eased myself from Benny's back to inspect both our wounds more closely. Benny held his left forefoot off the ground, resting his weight on the other three legs. The barbs seemed not to have torn any muscle but several layers of his thick skin had been ripped away. The bleeding began to lessen as I watched, but I knew the wound was painful.

My wonderful brave Benny, I thought, you're going to be stiff and sore for a while. I let Benny's reins drop to the ground and sat awkwardly in the cool alfalfa. My scratches were not too deep, thanks to my sturdy blue jeans, but they were throbbing and I knew that I, too, would be sore for several days.

Lorrie was the first to find his voice.

"Whew," he gasped, "is everybody okay?"

"Benny and I are a little torn up. Flesh wounds. Not deep. But we'll be all right. Let's just rest for a few minutes, shall we? Amy, are you okay?"

"I don't know, I don't know," she sobbed. She raised her head and looked at Lorrie and me through red eyes. "I don't know *what* to say."

74

Amy sniffled several times and blew her nose into a man-sized handkerchief. She finally brought her crying under control, dismounted from the dejected King, and sat in the grass beside us.

"Look what I've done to you and Benny! And look what The King almost did to me! We could have been killed! We could have killed you! I couldn't stop him. I tried and tried. I meant just to have a little race with you and look what happened!"

She burst into tears again, covering her face with her hands and the wadded-up handkerchief.

"Well, Goldie's okay. She's just tired and winded," Lorrie said, keeping his voice normal. "We kind of jerked up The King's mouth, I'm afraid, but that should heal in a jiffy. It's Benny who's been hurt the most. Will he be all right, Norma, do you think?"

"I'll get the vet out, Lorrie, to be on the safe side, but I'm pretty sure he'll be okay. Benny has a pretty tough constitution and I don't think this will get him down at all. He just needs a good rest right about now. But then, don't we all?"

"Oh, Norma, I'm so sorry for what I did to you and Benny," Amy wailed. "I guess The King and I were wrong. If anything serious comes of Benny's wound, I'll just die."

"Thinking back on it," Lorrie said, "just goes to show that Benny is really speedy. He left Goldie so far behind when he took off, she didn't have a prayer of catching him. And did you notice how he turned The King? Just the way he probably turned a stubborn calf in his younger days. Wasn't he something!" Lorrie emphasized each sentence with a shake of his head.

I could see Lorrie was filled with new admiration for a horse who was supposed to be getting old. Benny's ears perked up at the mention of his name, but I said nothing. I was feeling too tired—but I was proud of Benny.

It was Amy who brought our rest to an end.

"We'd better be heading for home," she said. "We have to take it slowly and it's getting close to supper time."

"Norma," Lorrie said, "you ride Goldie and I'll lead Benny."

We must have looked forlorn as we made our way back across the field. But Benny had won another round, and I knew that even Amy must admit now that he was the best horse of the three.

SEVEN

No Hobbles for Benny

S ome cowhand out west a long time ago had taught Benny to remain standing in one spot whenever his reins were dropped to the ground. It was funny about Benny. He *never* allowed his reins to be wrapped around a post or a tree. I had learned *that* the hard way the day I tied him to a sapling and he sat on his haunches and yanked.

But the moment his reins touched the ground, it was as though he were lashed to the spot by an invisible rope. He would graze contentedly, wandering no more than a few feet from the spot where the reins were dropped. He would nibble the grass in a circle around his imaginary post. If he happened to step on a rein, instead of jerking his head up and having a tug-of-war between his mouth and his weight on the rein, as most horses do, he shifted his weight a bit, raised the guilty hoof, pulled the reins forward with a toss of his head and continued grazing.

After the first few years of working and playing with Benny, I discovered that he had no objection at all to being staked out. Grandpa attached several feet of chain to a ring on top of a long iron spike. The spike was driven into the ground so that only the swiveling ring was visible. This prevented Benny's chain from getting twisted or wound around the spike, thus shortening the circumference of his grazing area.

If he found himself straddling the chain, most times he ignored it, unless he had played it out to its full length. In that case, again, instead of frightening himself into tangling his legs, he calmly lowered his nose to the grass and gingerly stepped over the chain.

Benny was as remarkable at figuring out his logistical problems as he was with other things. He seemed, in fact, to have a very analytical mind.

Eventually I discovered still a third way of tying Benny. After having read scores of cowboy and horse books, I was ashamed the idea hadn't occurred to me sooner. The discovery was the direct result of a less efficient method which we also tried.

Lost Valley belonged to the farm next to ours. It was a lovely wooded valley with high hills and a meandering stream through some pasture. Amy, Lorrie and I were allowed to ride in it as long as we kept our promise not to play roundup with the Holstein cows. The three of us often rode to a small island made by the branching stream where the grass grew knee-high. The ground was soft and moist where the branches of the stream rejoined and two fallen trees made a comfortable backrest for us. It was a wonderful private retreat where we could discuss such important subjects as horses, school, teachers, movies and movie stars, and horses.

As our conversations grew longer because we had more and more to talk about, the horses became restless. Sitting on the ground holding the reins was not a solution. The horses interrupted us constantly with their pulling and snorting. We would either have to find a way of giving the horses more grazing room or cut our discussions short. Turning the horses loose would mean that we'd end up walking home. Benny was happy to ground tie for a short time but not for this long. Goldie and The King wouldn't ground tie at all.

We tried making a small rope corral out of some

old clothesline, strips of leather, vines, and branches. But the three horses were too smart for that: the corral lasted no more than half an hour. Benny pulled the branches down as he nibbled on the leaves. Goldie leaned across the clothesline to eat the grass, which was always greener on the outside, and snapped it in two. The King rubbed a fly from his shoulder on a length of old leather and stretched it enough so that he could step over it.

"I have it," yelled Lorrie. "Why didn't we think of it sooner?"

"What's that?" Amy and I asked together.

"Why don't we hobble the horses? At least if they do wander off, they can't go very far or very fast. And there'd be no running away. They couldn't any of them move their legs more than a few inches at a time.

"That's a great idea," I said.

"We can even use some of the stuff we brought to make our corral out of," Amy suggested.

We went to work cheerfully and managed to salvage enough lengths of clothesline and leather strips to make three crude hobbles.

"Maybe we'd better run a little experiment on Benny first to see how he reacts. I imagine he's had hobbles on before. If he hasn't, it won't do any good to use them. But if he has and doesn't object, then it'll be easier to get The King and Goldie to wear them. I'll bet they've never had hobbles on at all."

"I suppose you're right," Amy said. "We can try The King second because Goldie's the most temperamental. If Benny and The King take to them, there won't be any problem with Goldie."

I knelt down beside Benny's slim forelegs and wound the strips of old leather loosely around his pasterns. Not sure how much slack to leave between each hoof, I guessed at a foot and a half. I tied the knot as firmly as possible, allowing some play so that the leather wouldn't irritate Benny's black pasterns and coronets, the bony area just above his hooves.

Benny looked at me questioningly and rubbed his lip in my hair. I raised up and stepped back to see what he would do. Benny continued watching me for a moment longer, then lowered his head and began to graze again.

"I think it's going to work," I whispered. "But the only way I can really tell is to take his bridle off. In case something goes wrong, if his hobbles come loose or something, keep a tight hold on Goldie and The King so Benny won't take off for home."

I slipped the bridle over Ben's ears, the bit clanking slightly as it slid past his teeth. I walked a few yards away, pretending to ignore him. Benny watched me for a minute, glanced around at The King and Goldie, then quietly resumed his grazing. He moved forward a few steps and I noticed that his normal step was shortened by several inches but he was completely unconcerned and quite comfortable.

"Great! No problem with Benny," Lorrie said. "One down, two to go. Let's get to work on The King."

Amy deftly attached her handmade hobbles to The King's pasterns. The King was a little confused at first by his sudden inability to take his usual step but he accepted the hobbles and, like Benny, became indifferent to them. Then, Goldie's long white ankles were bound and, to no one's surprise, she didn't fuss at all.

But I was to learn another lesson from Benny.

Late that summer, shortly before school started, Ben and I rode alone to Lost Valley. I was leaning comfortably against one of the tree trunks in our private retreat, watching some starlings flock noisily in a tree, when I glanced over at Benny to see if he was paying any attention to the chatter of the birds. He was gone! I didn't worry. In hobbles he couldn't have got very far and he would have to move slowly.

But it was getting late so I decided to put his bridle back on and head for home, once I caught up with him.

I saw that he had crossed the shallow stream and was working his way toward the farm. I jumped over the water and climbed the hill on the other side, Benny's bridle slung over my shoulder. When I reached the top of the hill, I gazed down through the trees and was amazed at the distance Benny had put between us. He wasn't *grazing* in the *direction* of the farm, he was literally hopping along, rabbit fashion, as fast as the hobbles would let him.

"Benny!" I shouted. "Wait for me! You crazy horse! Stop!"

He did stop—momentarily—to look back at me long enough to decide not to wait, for back he went to his absurd mincing hop.

I ran headlong down the hill, around bushes and trees, avoiding gopher holes, startling the cows until, breathless, I caught up with him. I slipped the reins of the bridle behind his ears and brought him to a stop.

"I guess I'll always have to learn the hard way about you, you crazy animal. I'd almost forgotten how darned ornery and independent you are."

I put the bit in his mouth, removed the hobbles and climbed into the saddle. We walked briskly back to the farm and I never again tried hobbles on Benny unless he had Goldie and The King to keep him company.

EIGHT

Homecoming

I was now fourteen and had changed a lot in the
five years Benny had been around. But Benny,
who was in his twenties, had not changed at all, either
in his appearance or his actions.

That year, autumn and school rolled around faster
than it ever had before. Now I was in high school
and I began to like everything better. For some
reason, the subjects were more interesting; the teachers had personalities. I made more friends and joined
more clubs. Football games and pep rallies were exciting. The school paper began to mention people I
actually knew.

Suddenly, other horizons expanded, too. I was familiar with Flint, the large industrial city eight miles from Grand Blanc. But Bendle, Mt. Morris, Fenton, Holly, and some other towns had been only names to me. Now I discovered that all of them sponsored amateur horse shows every summer, and I realized what a wonderful opportunity this would be for me and Benny. We'd work together all winter so that by summer we'd both be in top shape and maybe take some blue ribbons. After school and on weekends Benny and I could concentrate on figure eights, quick starts and stops, and on horsemanship generally. Long before the shows, I'd have to find out how Benny reacted to strange horses and crowds. But I couldn't think of a way to do that.

Soon after school started, notices began appearing in the school paper and posters were displayed on the bulletin boards encouraging students to join committees to help with Homecoming activities. Homecoming would be held the last Friday in October. Although most social events and special projects were sponsored by one class or another, Homecoming was so big an undertaking it required the time and talents of the whole school.

Committees were formed by the dozen. One was

responsible for planning the parade route. (The parade was the first event of the day.) Other committees handled the details of the pep rally and the snake dance through Grand Blanc. The bonfire in the evening required still another committee to scavenge for wood and kindling and to enforce safety rules. A special cheering committee was organized each year to make sure our students practiced in advance of the games and would not disgrace our team. The band cleaned their uniforms and polished their instruments. We spent several afternoons practicing marching formations for the half-time entertainment and many evenings in the music room practicing victory songs.

Another committee ran the contest to choose the Homecoming Queen and her court and worked out the ceremony for crowning her. They were also responsible for the special presentations to be made during half-time. The evening was to culminate in a Homecoming Dance—we hoped it would be a Homecoming *Victory* Dance and that our team would beat Fenton.

There was so much to do, so many committees to choose among, that our class couldn't decide which to be on. It would all be fun. Since we were lowly freshmen, why not work on the freshman float for the parade? There were prizes for the best floats and we'd have a chance to show just how clever and grown up we were.

After several chaotic class meetings during home-room period, three boys and three girls were chosen as the float committee. I was one of the three girls and was asked to be chairman, with Mr. Mason, one of the English teachers, acting as co-chairman and advisor.

Our first act was to set up a meeting for the first free hour we all had.

I knew all the members of my committee quite well. The other two girls, Barbara Burek and Sally Gundry, and I became close friends after our first meetings and remained close friends. Harvey Samson, a very short boy, even shorter than I was, had a round, very merry face. I could see that Harvey wasn't going to let the committee get too serious. Donald Graham, nicknamed Pluto because of his long sloping ears, would offset Harvey's frivolity with his seriousness. Albert Foster I knew only by sight. He was doing below average work in school but he seemed to have an intense interest in the freshman float. Albert lived not far from me and had often waved to Benny and me from his bicycle.

After a few rudimentary instructions on parliamentary procedure, the first committee meeting got under way. Our first job was to decide on a theme for the float. Harvey suggested we make two football teams out of papier-mâché and show ours victorious over Fenton.

"But that's probably what most of the floats will be like," Barbara said. "Why don't we try to think of something a little more original?"

"I'm sure we've got enough ideas and then some to come up with something really imaginative," Pluto said.

"We don't have to stick to the football theme, do we? I mean we can branch out a little from that, can't we?" Sally asked.

"Of course we can. What do you suggest?"

Mr. Mason came to our rescue at that point. "May I make a suggestion, Miss Chairman?"

"Oh, please, Mr. Mason."

"Perhaps the best way to go about deciding on a theme would be to draw up a list of ideas which could be checked out for cost, availability of materials, probable number of hours required to make it and other pertinent factors. Then, if this committee agrees, the list could be presented to the whole freshman class, with recommendations from this committee, for its vote."

Mr. Mason sat down again and waited for us to continue.

"That sounds like a very good suggestion, Mr.

Mason. We thank you." I turned to the committee. "Does this meet with your approval?" All five nodded.

"Since it's so close to the end of the period, why don't we adjourn but promise to take a little time between now and our next meeting to think of some good themes? Please write them down and bring them with you. Maybe then we'll be able to come up with something." I glanced at Mr. Mason, having suddenly forgotten how to adjourn a meeting in parliamentary style.

"Ask for a motion to adjourn, Norma," he whispered as he moved toward me at the front of the room. I guessed this wasn't the first freshman committee he'd ever advised.

Barbara and Sally waited for me in the hall and we walked to our next class together.

"We've really got to think of something super-special," Sally said, "something really neat."

"We've just got to win the prize. Wouldn't it be fun if we could beat all the other classes?" Barbara asked.

"What I'd like most about winning," I said, "would be to show Howdy. He thinks there's no class in the whole school but the seniors. He's not on the senior float committee but he knows what they're planning and he won't tell me. He won't even give me a hint."

"I know just how you feel," Sally said. "My sister's

a sophomore and she won't tell me anything either. Oh well, when we decide what it will be, we'll just keep ours secret, too."

The next meeting began in an orderly fashion but parliamentary rules were forgotten as discussions got heated and we argued about one another's suggestions for the float. Mr. Mason sat quietly in the back of the classroom, speaking only when he thought our voices might be carrying into the hall.

It was Albert Foster, surprisingly, who came up with an idea that appealed to us all.

"Why don't we do something that's pretty but simple? I mean simple to make?" he asked. "Something that all of us could help do, if you know what I mean. After all, the float will be carrying our class's nomination for Homecoming queen, so it can't be too crude looking. I mean it wouldn't look right, would it, to have a rough-looking float with a pretty girl on it?"

Albert looked embarrassed and wouldn't raise his eyes to look at us. But he did go on. "I'll bet the other classes will come up with something that has to do with football or Hallowe'en. That's what the floats are usually about every year. But ours will be better than that." No one interrupted because Albert spoke so seldom. We had all thought he was either not interested or very shy. "Maybe something along the

southern line. You know . . . the southern belle idea."
He couldn't go on. He leaned back in his seat, looking almost ashamed to have spoken for so long.

Albert's suggestion put a spark to our imaginations. We all began talking at once. Mr. Mason rose from his seat and walked to the front of the room where he remained standing until we had quieted down a little.

"Let's try to keep our voices down to a dull roar," he said. "Albert's idea is good but let's not shout it all over the school—yet." He waited a few seconds until there was complete silence. "Now then, shall we proceed as though we were a little more civilized and see what can be worked out?"

Mr. Mason always seemed tired when he spoke, never angry, but weary, as though the committee exhausted him. He turned the meeting back to me.

"Okay, gang, maybe we should try talking about the southern belle idea one at a time," I said. "Who's first? Do you want to add anything, Albert? After all, it's your idea."

"Oh no, you go ahead and talk about it. It's just an idea and probably not worth much anyhow." Albert's face flushed scarlet and he looked at me as though I had been picking on him.

"No, Albert, it's a very good idea. Harv?"

"If we could get a flat-bed truck or a good-sized

trailer and tractor, we'd have enough room to put a nice southern scene on it."

Pluto's hand shot up and I nodded permission for him to speak. "We could get good ideas from pictures in magazines and maybe we could paint a colonial house to use as a backdrop."

"How on earth would you get a whole house on a float?" Barbara asked innocently.

"I don't mean a real house, silly, just the *front* of a colonial house—pillars, windows and door. You know. And it doesn't have to be life-size, either, to look real."

"That's right and we could even make a couple of papier-mâché trees with that grey stuff that hangs from the branches," Sally added.

"Spanish moss," Pluto said.

"And the freshman candidate for queen could ride on the float and be dressed like a real southern belle," Sally said.

"Don't forget we have to submit our ideas to the rest of the class for approval," I pointed out. "Let's work out this idea as best we can and maybe work on a couple of others too. We have to wait and see what the rest of the class votes before we can start buying material and working on it."

The Southern Belle, as it came to be called, was approved by the whole class as soon as we'd explained it and our reasons for choosing it. The class was sworn to secrecy. We could hardly wait to get started on it.

At the next committee meeting, Albert again made a suggestion. This one startled and excited me.

"I've been thinking since our last meeting. We could make the float even more realistic if we could maybe get Norma to ride her horse alongside it, done up in southern style, too. It would make people think of a plantation, if you know what I mean."

"Albert, that's a great idea," Pluto cut in. "There are always horses in parades, so why not ours?"

Sally, Harvey and Barbara agreed.

"Well, if it's okay with my folks, it's okay with me," I said.

Here was my chance—and how unexpected!—to get Benny acquainted with crowds. I hoped with all my heart that my parents would let me do it.

NINE

Parade Plans

That night after dinner, I broached the subject just as Mom and Pop were drinking their second cups of coffee. Howdy had already left the table, anxious to get the love seat in front of the television before I did.

"The Homecoming plans for our float are really coming along great," I said slowly.

"That's nice, Norma. Can you tell us what your theme is?" Mom asked. Pop smiled at me, waiting for me to elaborate.

"Well, just so you don't tell Howdy. He won't tell me what his class is doing."

"I don't think he cares much about floats," Pop said. "When he gets time out from his studies he is more interested in football and the big game."

Howdy was preparing himself for pre-law and college. He wanted to go to William and Mary in Virginia.

"Yes, but you know how he is. I won't have any peace if he finds out what our plans are."

"Norma, you have our word. We're sworn to secrecy. We won't let on we know a thing, will we, dear?"

"No, of course not." Pop leaned back in his ladder-back chair while Mom and I began clearing the table.

I explained the Southern Belle idea to them, omitting only the suggestion that I ride Benny in the parade. As I told them of the setting—the plantation house, the trees with Spanish moss, the green carpeting for grass, the wrought-iron chair painted white to seat the freshman candidate for queen—I could see that they thought the idea was good.

"It sounds lovely, Norma," Mom said. "Will there by anyone else on the float besides the candidate for queen?" Mom rinsed the glasses carefully with steaming hot water from the old tea kettle. As I began wiping them, I sensed this was the perfect moment to tell about me riding Benny.

"Yes, there will be. A couple of fellows seated on

the ground alongside her." I picked up another hot glass, pushed my fist wrapped in the dish towel inside it to dry it, and without looking up said, "It has even been suggested that I ride Benny alongside the float, all done up in southern style, to give it the finishing touch."

I found that I had been holding my breath. I released it slowly.

Without so much as a glance at each other, Mom and Pop both said, "That would be nice."

I nearly dropped the glass.

"You mean I can? You mean you'll let me?" I wondered if they had heard me right.

Pop looked at me, a little surprised at my questions. "I don't know why not, if you want to. You've been riding long enough now and you know Benny pretty well. I doubt that the crowd will frighten Benny or make him shy and throw you, so I see no reason why not."

Drying the dishes and putting them away, ordinarily a dreary chore, went like a breeze that night. As soon as I'd finished I rushed out to tell the news to Benny.

There was less than a month to prepare and every day seemed to have wings. After school, whenever I didn't have a committee meeting or a lot of homework, Benny and I rode in the long alfalfa fields, practicing what we hoped was a parade gait. At first, Benny was perfectly happy jogging along at a relaxed pace but as the day came nearer, Benny caught a little of my fever. His steps became springier and lighter, he tucked his chin in and arched his neck a little more. Benny was turning out to be a natural for the parade. He loved to show off.

But not me. I would get a thousand butterflies in my stomach whenever I thought of the crowd. I hoped Benny's self-assurance wouldn't evaporate as mine undoubtedly would when the spectators and the noise were a reality.

Amy and Lorrie rode with me often. I confided in them my part in the parade. They were almost as excited as I was. They would stand to one side as Benny and I practiced our parade gait and offer tactful hints and criticism. Even with so small and familiar an audience, Benny realized he was being called upon for a special performance. With each practice session he became a little flashier. I was encouraged by his showmanship.

To my surprise, Albert Foster was a constant visitor to these sessions. He had no horse to ride, so he would bounce along beside us on his bicycle, stopping occasionally to pull grass from his bicycle chain. Very often he would delay going home until long after Lorrie and Amy had left, talking to Grandpa and me as we finished up the evening chores.

"I didn't know you liked horses so well, Albert," I said one night as I threw some fresh yellow wheat straw around the two box stalls.

"I didn't know I did either, until I saw you riding Benny around," he said.

I remembered that the first time he had rubbed his hand along Benny's smooth neck was the only time I had ever seen his lips move toward a smile. "Yes, I do like Benny—a lot," he said.

"Don't you like Goldie?"

"She's okay but she's not like Benny." Albert's eyes followed Benny as I let him into his stall from the barnyard for the night. "Where did you get Benny?" He leaned against the half-door of Benny's stall, watching his strong jaws grind up the oats.

"Some friends of ours gave him to us. Earl and

Howdy used to ride him but they got tired of it after a while. Then Grandpa taught me to ride and I guess Benny's mine now."

"I'd never get tired of riding Benny," he said, his gaze fastened on Benny.

"I don't think I will either, Albert. He's a wonderful horse."

Albert nodded glumly, then asked, "Would you ever sell him?"

"Oh no," I answered quickly. I brushed off some wisps of straw clinging to my wool shirt and as I glanced up, I saw that Albert had switched his gaze from Benny to me. His look was unmistakable. He *hated* me.

"Well, I guess I'd better get on home." He walked slowly to the barn door.

"Albert, what's the matter? Are you mad at me? Because I don't want to sell Benny to you? I wouldn't sell him to anyone! For anything."

"I'd like to own Benny! He should be mine!" With that announcement, which he shouted at me, he strode out of the barn and down the road, pushing his bicycle, kicking at pebbles. I watched him until the darkness covered him and I could see him no more.

Grandpa came from behind the barn where he'd been throwing forkfuls of hay to the hungry cattle.

"What's got Albert so upset?"

"I don't really know, Grandpa. He seems different,

not the way he was at our committee meetings. He gave me a bad look and stalked off when I told him I would never sell Benny to him or anyone else."

"That boy must like horses an awful lot, but 'tain't healthy wanting something that bad, 'specially when it belongs to someone else."

Grandpa touched the pocket of his blue cotton work shirt to make sure he hadn't lost his package of tobacco in the hay. I gave Benny and Goldie a final fond pat, then Grandpa pulled the master switch that turned the electricity in the barn on and off. Darkness dropped on us and we both listened for a moment to the soft sounds of the horses pulling at the hay, to the beefy steers pushing each other to get closer to the hayrack, and the pigeons cooing softly high up in the old oak rafters.

We stepped out into the chilly October night and I waited while Grandpa fastened the latches on the barn doors. We had no locks on these doors. There were too many ways to get into the barn, locks or no locks. The doors were secured as well as possible, more to keep out the weather than visitors.

"How're you and Benny coming along with your practice for the parade?" Grandpa asked.

The morose feeling Albert had left me with vanished at the thought of the parade. "It's coming just fine, Grandpa. I think Benny will do very well. I'm probably the one who'll be scared stiff."

"You'll both be fine. I haven't a doubt of that. You can count on me, you know. I want to see this. I'll be watching you, along with your folks."

"Good, Grandpa. I'll be looking for you as we ride down Grand Blanc Road. Be sure to clap loudest for our float. The winner will be announced at half-time during the football game, just before they tell us who will be the Homecoming queen."

"I'll clap loud, Norma Jean, you can bet on that. We'll all be rooting for you *and* your float."

Grandpa climbed into his old car.

"Good night, Grandpa. See you in the morning."

"Good night, Norma Jean."

As he switched on his car lights, Grandpa's face was slightly furrowed in a frown. He was worried about something but I quickly forgot about it as he drove off. My mind was on the parade.

The ten days before the parade passed so quickly that they're all a blur, more like one long, long day than ten. After our committee had bought all the necessary materials for the float, the class voted to add more members to the committee and change its name to the Construction Committee. Every night after school, we worked tirelessly. We wanted to create the finest float ever to appear in a Homecoming parade in Grand Blanc.

I was excused from the last two evenings of work to get Benny and myself ready for our special roles. I asked Mom to mend a costume Mr. Mason had borrowed from the drama department for me.

Howdy, although busy with football practice and not around the house too much, had been able to figure out what our float would represent and proceeded to torment me about Benny's and my shortcomings and how everybody would laugh at us in the parade. He added to my misery by dropping hints about the beauties of the senior class float. Pop remained relatively calm during these baiting sessions but on more than one evening he stopped reading his newspaper or watching a favorite television program to silence Howdy or to subdue my high spirits.

The entire student body was almost impossible to control during the last week. The students were tense and working hard. Each of us was confident his class would win first prize in the float contest; and all of us were certain our team would crush Fenton in the game.

To my delight, Barbara Burek was elected freshman class candidate for Homecoming queen. She and I talked about nothing but the parade every moment we were together.

Albert stopped coming to the farm. I was sorry he was angry at me but not sorry he had stopped coming. I saw him occasionally in school, or as I rode Benny past his house, but he never said hello.

Two evenings before the parade, as Benny and I were doing our final practice in the alfalfa field with Lorrie and Amy watching, I noticed that Albert was leaning solemnly against his bicycle at the edge of the road. I pulled Benny to a stop and motioned him to join us. Instead, he leaned more resolutely on his bike. Amy and Lorrie also waved to him but he remained stolidly aloof and silent. As Lorrie on Goldie rode toward him to talk with him, Albert abruptly hopped on his bike and pedaled furiously toward his house.

"I wonder what's the matter with him, anyhow? I wonder why he seems to be so mad at me?" I asked, as much of myself as of Amy and Lorrie. They both shrugged their shoulders and I once again dismissed Albert from my mind.

The next day was Thursday, the day before Homecoming. The conversation in school was all about the parade, the football game, the candidates for queen, the floats, the dance. Nobody mentioned studies.

Even the teachers were caught up in the excitement. Many of them had helped us to coordinate committees, plans and work. Thursday afternoon was devoted to last minute details and Mr. Mason called our float committee together for its final meeting.

"Everything seems to be in fine shape, so there really wasn't any practical need to call this meeting," Mr. Mason said in his weary voice, "but I called it because I wanted to tell you that I think you've done a wonderful job on the float." We smiled. "You've all put in a lot of time and energy trying to create a float that would be more original and beautiful than any of the others. I may be just a little prejudiced, and I haven't seen any of the other floats, but I want you to know that I'm confident the Southern Belle will win."

We applauded Mr. Mason and thanked him. We felt that he must be—he had to be—right.

Then I noticed that Albert wasn't at the meeting. I wondered where he was and whether he hadn't come because of me. I resolved then to make a special effort to mend the breach as soon as I had time, as soon as the parade and the game and the dance were over.

Mr. Mason continued his praise a few minutes longer and again I slipped Albert Foster to the back of my mind but less easily than I had before. There was just something about him that bothered me, something besides the fact that he seemed angry at me.

Immediately after school that day Grandpa and I gave Benny a bath. I led Benny from the barn across the road to the back yard where Grandpa and I had set up an orderly work-line—two pails of sudsy water, several brushes for scrubbing, the regular brush and curry comb for the mane and tail, scissors for trimming, blueing to add to the water to brighten Benny's silky coat, pails of lukewarm rinse water, black shoe polish to paint Benny's three black hoofs, and Mom's clear nail polish to put a gloss on Benny's one white hoof, old turkish towels scavenged from Mom's rag bag to rub him dry, and, last of all, his stable blanket (of which he had grown no fonder) to keep him from catching cold after the bath and to keep him clean when he was stabled for the night. The jar of brilliantine we put out, too, though we wouldn't apply it until just before the parade to bring out the shine in Benny's clean coat.

The moment I led Benny around the corner of the house, I knew it was going to be a battle to give him a bath. As soon as he spotted all the paraphernalia, he jerked up short, nearly pulling me backwards to the ground. His ears went forward and his eyes widened as he looked over all the equipment spread out on the lawn.

"Look, Grandpa, Benny knows right away all that stuff has something to do with him. He doesn't want to go near it." I laughed.

Benny pulled back on the lead rein but when he felt resistance, he looked again. "Hoping, the way I sometimes have hoped," Grandpa said, "that if I stared long enough at something I didn't like, it would go away.

"Come on, Ben," Grandpa cajoled. "There's nothin' there that'll bother you. Norma and I just want to give you a nice warm bath, so you'll look your best for the parade. You don't know it but you've got a big special day ahead of you."

Benny paid absolutely no attention to Grandpa's pleading. Nothing we said or did succeeded in getting Benny one step nearer his bath.

"Well, Norma, like Mohammed and the mountain, if he won't go near the bath, we'll have to bring the bath over to him."

Grandpa picked up the two pails of soapy water and two brushes, setting one down on each side of Ben. Benny's neck descended and he cocked his ears first toward one pail then the other. He wanted nothing to do with any bubble bath! He was neither frightened nor shy but these human shenanigans made him indignant.

As I reached down and dipped the brush into the foamy water, Ben backed up the length of the lead rein. This maneuver made it impossible for me to reach any farther back than his shoulder. Grandpa picked up his pail and stepped back with Benny, continuing to work up a rich lather along Benny's wither.

"Grandpa, what'll I do? I can't tie him up. You know what he'd do. And a long stake-out would be useless too."

Grandpa stopped scrubbing and leaned against

Benny, one arm draped over Ben's back, the water dripping from the end of the brush.

"Looks like we'll have to have a little more help. You go in the house and see if you can get Howdy out here to hold the lead strap."

I dropped the brush into my pail and the lead rein to the ground and dashed into the house. I interrupted Howdy's "training" (he was lolling comfortably on the love seat, watching a mystery on television) and when we appeared on the back porch, we found Grandpa seated on the ground with the lead strap in his hand, laughing so hard that he couldn't chew his tobacco.

Benny stood with his forelegs slightly apart, his head turned toward his hindquarters. When we saw what Benny had done, Howdy and I couldn't help laughing either. His left hind leg was in my pail, white soap bubbles clinging to it. Benny was staring at it, trying to decide his next move. On Ben's other side sat Grandpa, in a pool of foam. Grandpa's overalls were soaked.

Grandpa slapped his legs until the bubbles disappeared but the wet overalls clung to his thin legs, making him look a little like a ballet dancer in tights. This made me laugh still harder. Howdy doubled over, his arms across his stomach, and Grandpa's old-fashioned glasses were wet with tears. Benny, too, seemed to enjoy the hilarity: he raised his upper lip and thrust his nose in the air.

"Nothing like giving us the horse laugh," I gasped.

"All he did," Grandpa said, "was just swing around to walk back to the barn. But when he did, he knocked me over into my scrub pail. The whole thing spilled all over me. Then, when he felt himself bump against me, he swung back to the other side and ended up sticking his hind hoof in your pail."

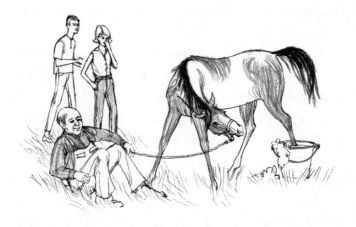

When I got control of myself, I lifted Benny's leg out of the pail and moved the pail a safe distance away. Howdy took the lead strap from Grandpa as Mom came out and gave us refills of sudsy water. Grandpa and I went back to bathing Ben who still tried to back up. No amount of tugging or cajoling on Howdy's part could convince Ben either to move forward or to stand still. Eventually, Benny backed himself up against the side of the house where he had no choice but to submit to the bath.

"You'd think we beat him or something, the way he stands there looking at us," I said and laughed.

"I don't really blame him," Howdy said. "Who'd want to have this kind of a bath anyway?"

"You're right, Howdy. This isn't exactly Benny's cup of tea and it's probably the first time in his life for this kind of a bath. I'll bet he'd give a romp in the pasture to be some place else."

Benny kept a sharp eye on us. His ears, spotted by the water splashing from his neck, worked rhythmically back and forth, not missing a beat. As he shifted his weight from one hind leg to the other, I could see he was tempted to try another swing sideways. Three of us and the house behind him discouraged him, however, until, finally, he resigned himself and stood completely still. In a matter of minutes, he was almost leaning into the brushes: now that the initial shock was over, he was enjoying his scrub.

"Just like a massage, hey, Benny?" Howdy asked. Although Howdy was no longer interested in riding, his hand rubbed Benny's nose affectionately.

When we sloshed Ben with the rinse water, he stiffened with shock and distaste but as soon as the final rubbing with the rough turkish towels began, he relaxed and stuck out his upper lip to show his pleasure.

Benny looked beautiful. The blueing in the bath water brought out the hidden sheen in his white spots. His mane glistened and his black forelock fell softly between his eyes. His perky ears looked smaller and his fetlocks curved smoothly once we had clipped and trimmed the long hair around them. We could almost see our reflections in his hooves after the manicure— or would it be pedicure?

Benny looked beautiful and he knew it. His steps were springier as I led him around the yard in his blanket until I was sure he was dry. He tossed his head playfully, begging me for sugar. We put him back in his stall, hoping he'd leave his blanket alone just this one night so that he would look clean for the parade tomorrow.

I had the final fitting of my costume to attend to and Howdy wanted to rest some more for the game, so Grandpa said good night to us and we watched him drive his old car back through the fields, a cloud of dust behind him, before we went into the house.

TEN

Gone!

B y this time I was so keyed up I knew I would lie awake all night. But I must have dropped off to sleep almost as soon as I stretched out in my warm bed.

It seemed about ten minutes later that someone was shaking my shoulder, trying to wake me. I sat up in bed and rubbed the sleep from my eyes.

"Oh, it's you, Pop. Is it time to get up already? It's still dark outside."

"No, it's still early. But I think you and I had better go over to the barn."

"Why, what's the matter?" Then I heard the

whinny. "That's Goldie," I said. "What's the matter with her? She doesn't usually whinny unless I take Benny away from her for a ride."

Suddenly I was wide awake. Something had happened to Benny! I jumped out of bed, into some shoes, and slipped my wool robe over my pajamas.

"I heard the whinnying," Pop said. "I couldn't tell whether it was Benny or Goldie, so I thought I'd better wake you up. I'm sure there's nothing wrong but it won't hurt to check."

We slipped quietly out the front door, bundled in our overcoats to protect us from the cold October night. The moon had set and the eastern horizon was beginning to brighten. It was later than I realized. The grass was wet with a heavy dew and, after a few steps, our damp pajamas slapped against our ankles.

"Pop! Look! The barn door's open!"

We broke into a trot across the road and plunged into the darkness of the barn. Pop flipped the switch for the electricity and as the lights came on, Goldie welcomed us with a lonesome nicker. Benny's head was not poking over his stall door. I rushed to look over it to see if he was lying down. Benny's grain box was empty and half the water in his pail was gone. The leafy portions of his hay had been eaten, the longer coarser stems pushed to one side. Then I noticed that the straw on the floor of the stall was matted and disheveled and the gate to the stall was shut as securely as it had been when I had left him after his bath. But there was no Benny!

"Where could he have gone? How did he get out?" I asked tremulously, biting my lip to keep it from quivering.

"Don't worry, Norma, I'm sure we'll have it all figured out in a minute." Pop rubbed Goldie's nose thoughtfully, then he said, "It's obvious that he didn't just open the gate himself, walk out, then close it behind him, even though the outside barn door is open. Let's look around a bit."

We walked into the feed room and the tack room, flicking on the light switches as we went. The cobwebs were a net around the light bulbs. The feed room partitions cast eerie shadows. In the tack room, I pointed.

"Look, Pop, there's Benny's blanket, all neatly folded up and hung over the blanket rack."

I could keep my tears back no longer. Pop put his arm around my shoulders and waited until I could get hold of myself.

"Goldie's bridle is here but Benny's is gone. His saddle is here, though," Pop said. "Whoever took him must have slipped the bridle on right over his halter and ridden away bareback."

I couldn't stop crying.

"Come on, Norma. He can't have been gone too long. We'll call Grandpa and get Howdy up. We'll all do some searching. If we can't find him, we'll call the police."

The ground outside the barn gave no clues. The night had frozen it into a crust.

When Grandpa and Howdy arrived, Pop and Howdy jumped into our car and drove west on Cook Road. Grandpa and I began our search to the east.

The sun rose over the horizon and Grandpa flicked off his car lights. Looking was easier now. We drove slowly, keeping a sharp watch ahead and in the fields to right and left for a movement or a sign. We listened for a whinny from Ben. A light mist rose from the black dirt of the low ground as the sun warmed the cold frost.

I was no longer crying but my mind was a whirl of horrible thoughts. Out of this jungle of thoughts came an idea. Of course! Why hadn't I thought of it before?

"Grandpa, do you suppose that Albert Foster could have . . . ?"

Grandpa glanced at me quickly and nodded. "Yes, Norma Jean, he could have. Very easily. Just to make sure, let's check his home."

Grandpa's foot pressed down on the accelerator and we sped over the spattering gravel road to Albert's small house.

Grandpa's heavy knock on the front door brought a shuffling to the front window where two tired eyes peeped out at us. Then the door was opened by a heavy dark-haired woman. Her hair was uncombed and she was wrapped in an old plaid bathrobe, one pocket torn off.

"Mrs. Foster?"

"What do you want at this hour of the morning?"

"I'm sorry to bother you, Mrs. Foster. I'm Norma Cline and this is my grandfather. Is Albert home?"

"Oh, for heaven's sakes, what's he done now?" she snapped.

Grandpa and I glanced at each other.

"Well, I don't . . . I'm not sure but . . . ." I stammered.

"Wait just a minute. I'll go see if he's here."

Mrs. Foster turned away from us and padded out of sight in her worn cloth slippers. I noticed that the living room had very little furniture and what there was needed repair and cleaning. Some toys were on the floor and the curtains were dingy.

"No, he ain't in his room," said Mrs. Foster, returning. "His bed's been slept in but he sometimes gets up and goes out real early. Don't ask me where because I don't know. I never do. Anyway, what's it got to do with you? You missing something?"

"Well, yes, I am. It's Benny, my horse. I know Albert liked him and I just wondered if he could have, uh, borrowed him for a while maybe."

Mrs. Foster frowned. "No, Albert never *borrows* nothin'. He's done this before but never nothing as big as a horse." She sighed and added, "I suppose this means he'll have to go back."

She caught the questioning looks on our faces and continued. "I guess you didn't know. Albert's sick, has been ever since he was a baby. In spells. He don't always know right from wrong. He never does nothing worse than stealin' little things, well, little, until your horse, that is, but every now and then he sort of forgets that he can't always have what ain't his, so he helps himself. Anyways, when he gets this way, I have to send him back to Lapeer."

My eyes widened at every word. The hospital for the care of the mentally ill was in Lapeer. I had no idea that Albert needed this kind of help and I was immediately ashamed of myself for not having shown him the patience and friendship he so needed.

"Do you know where he might have gone, Mrs. Foster?" Grandpa asked.

"No, but he never goes too far. He don't always come back the same day. Sometimes he likes to sleep out in the woods. But don't worry about your horse. He won't hurt him."

"Thank you very much, Mrs. Foster," Grandpa said, "we'll try to find him."

Grandpa and I walked quickly to the car and backed out of the driveway.

"We'll just keep looking up and down the roads for a while," Grandpa said as we drove off. "Then if we have no luck, you'd better saddle Goldie and I'll get the tractor and we'll search off the roads."

"Grandpa, I feel just terrible about Albert. I didn't realize there was something wrong with him—really wrong."

"I know you didn't, Norma. Neither did I. It's not your fault."

"Yes it is, in a way. I shouldn't have shut him and everything else that didn't have to do with the parade out of my mind." We rode in silence for a while as we scanned the countryside. "Grandpa, you know something?"

Grandpa looked at me and smiled.

"It seems as if I'm always learning something from Benny one way or another. I think he's teaching me more about things than I could ever teach him."

As we drove up in front of the barn, the sun was glinting off its silvery roof. The school buses would soon be rolling by. I felt a selfish pang of disappointment as I realized there was a strong possibility that Benny and I might not be riding in the parade. Pop and Howdy were waiting for us. I knew at a glance their search had been as unsuccessful as ours. Grandpa told them what we'd learned from Mrs. Foster.

While I hurriedly bridled and saddled Goldie, we decided that Howdy would go to school to let Mr. Mason know that I might not be there. Pop would continue searching by car, Grandpa would investigate the fields with the tractor, and I would explore the woods and other places where neither a tractor nor a car could go.

ELEVEN

The Search

Goldie cantered toward the woods, her white ears pricked sharply forward, listening for a familiar whinny from Benny. We raised no dust from the hard ground and Goldie's hoofbeats sounded unusually loud in the still morning air. We left the lane and moved across the alfalfa field to the woods. The wet grass swished around Goldie's legs and turned them a dark grey. We slowed to a walk as we entered the woods, moving as quietly as possible to catch every sound. Now Goldie's steps were muffled by the wet brown leaves and the only noise was the occasional caw of crows.

Goldie stopped and whinnied in full voice. She

stood with her head up, every sense alert, but there was no response. She started forward again slowly. We were following the little path that Benny and I had used so often. It wound in and out among the trees and bushes. We passed the spot where Benny had ripped his bridle from his head and left me stranded and furiously angry.

There was no sign of Benny—no hoof marks in the leaves or on the grass. No one had been on this path recently.

I called Benny's name often; less often, Albert's. Goldie whinnied and listened again. Our only reply was the rustle of a few dry leaves or the flight of a startled sparrow.

It grew warmer in the woods and glancing up through the bare trees, I saw that the sun was getting high. I knew that by now classes were in progress. There would be only half a day of school today and everybody would have a hard time, even so, concentrating on class work. The excitement would be reaching its height.

Satisfied that Benny and Albert had not been in the woods, Goldie and I turned and galloped back to the barn. For the first time in her life, Goldie was not anxious to go home. She was as concerned for Benny as I was. The tractor was not in the barn yet, neither was Pop's car.

Mom stepped out onto the porch, looking worried,

to tell me that she had been calling the neighbors to see if they had seen or heard anything. But no luck so far.

Goldie and I took off again, cantered west on Cook Road for a short distance, then turned down the lane leading back to Lost Valley. I dismounted to open the gate, led Goldie through and remounted. I noticed from the tracks around the watering trough that the Holsteins from the neighboring farm had been put out to pasture: there were no other tracks but theirs.

Goldie stepped lightly as we crossed the wooden bridge over the drainage ditch, then began to canter again.

The hunt for Albert and Benny was taking much longer than I had thought. I prayed that they were all right. I knew Benny would do nothing foolish or be mean to Albert but he would try to outthink him. Albert, however, worried me. If he wanted Benny badly enough to steal him, what might he not do to keep him? Maybe he had ridden Benny very far away. I pressed Goldie into a faster gallop and momentarily I was aware of thinking that she didn't have Benny's speed or endurance, though she wasn't nearly as old.

We galloped around the last fence post into the bright open field which stretched flat before us in the crisp sunshine until it plunged into the gorge—wide and deep—that was our Lost Valley. Though I was impatient, I reined Goldie down to her brisk slow gait. I didn't want to disturb the grazing cows. A few of them raised their heads and stared at us; some moved away but most of them ignored us and went placidly on, pulling at the short grass.

We picked up the canter again as we entered the valley until we reached the stream, the edges muddy where the cows had crossed back and forth through it. Goldie lowered her head and I allowed her a short drink. Then, from a standstill, she jumped the stream. Unlike Benny, Goldie never walked through water if she could avoid it.

"C'mon, Goldie, let's go up the hill to the highest point to see what we can see. I know you're getting tired but we can't give up now."

Goldie's neck was damp and her white hair along the edge of the saddle blanket and behind her ears was dark with sweaty dust. She grunted a little as her long legs carried us jerkily up the hill. As soon as she was facing out over the valley, she whinnied twice, long and loud.

Almost immediately there was a responding whinny. And another. It was Benny's! I recognized it at once. Goldie swung her head toward it and trotted along the edge of the hill, watching for a first sight of him. She picked her way gracefully around shrubs and trees while I kept busy ducking branches. I knew that Goldie's sensitive ears and her keen nose would get us to Benny more quickly than my guess.

Benny whinnied again and Goldie answered. They were asking and confirming directions, and in a language no human could understand. Goldie plunged recklessly down the hill while I clung to the pommel to keep from being thrown off. I prayed that she wouldn't end up going head over heels. Goldie took a sharp right around the bottom of the hill and stopped.

The grassy meadow where so many important decisions had been made by Lorrie, Amy and me no longer looked serene. It no longer invited tired riders and horses to make themselves comfortable around its two worn tree trunks or in the soft grass. The grass had been trampled into the earth except for a fringe or two at the edge of the stream. Mud had been stirred up in the brook and one of the tree trunks had been skinned of some of its bark. The loveliest spot in Lost Valley looked ravaged. And standing in the center of it were Benny and Albert.

My first concern was for Benny. I let my eyes look over his body for signs of cruelty or injury. I was relieved to see no marks on his glossy coat. The white spots still shone brilliantly from the blueing in his bath the night before. But his eyes were ringed with white, always a sign of fear, and his ears jerked nervously back and forth. He twitched his long black tail, stamping his hind feet on the torn ground, yet he kept his forelegs planted firmly, ready to pull back. Around Benny's neck was a heavy manila rope which led to Albert's bony hand, clutching the rope tight, his arm full length in front of him.

Albert stared at me with contempt. His lips were twitching a little and he wiped perspiration off his upper lip with the back of his free hand. Just as I opened my mouth to speak, Albert jerked savagely on the rope, causing Benny to tilt his head to one side. Benny's nostrils were flaring. Then I saw that Albert had tightened the noose around Benny's throat so that his breathing was labored.

"Albert!" I shrieked. "Look what you're doing! You're choking Benny."

Albert said nothing but he did relax the tension on the rope enough to let Benny get his head up straight again. The noose was still tight around his throat and his nostrils were still flared as he tried to get more air. Albert took a step toward Benny; Benny backed up a step, keeping Albert at the length of the rope.

I knew it would do no good to talk to Albert. And I couldn't decide whether to dismount and try to walk up to Benny. All I knew was that some way I had to loosen the deadly rope. I decided that staying on Goldie gave me an advantage.

Slowly I walked Goldie toward Albert. Albert

stared—glared is a more accurate word—and I was frightened for Benny. I tried not to show it because I wanted Albert to think I wasn't afraid. Benny's eyes darted from Albert to me. It seemed as though he was waiting for a cue that would tell him his next move. Albert watched our approach warily but he did not budge. Again, he wiped the sweat, despite the cool October weather, from his upper lip.

I stopped Goldie a few feet short of Albert. I tried to put Goldie at an angle between Benny and Albert that would make it possible for me to charge Albert and force him to drop Benny's rope if I had to. I leaned over Goldie's neck and stretched my open palm toward Albert's hand.

Albert's eyes shifted from my face to my hand. Slowly he brought the end of the rope up to meet my hand. His icy fingers touched mine as he dropped the rope into my palm. Then he sank to the muddy ground.

The moment the rope left Albert's hand, Benny walked up beside Goldie and I leaned over to loosen the strangling grip of the rope from his throat. Benny rubbed his nose and cheek against my leg and greeted Goldie happily with his soft nicker.

As I was wondering what to do about Albert, he stood up and spoke as though he had read my mind.

"I guess it's time I was going home," he whispered. "Benny doesn't want me. He only wants you." Tears ran down his cheeks, mixing with the sweat and mud on his face, and he walked stiffly toward home as though he was pushing his body over the ground against every wish of his heart.

Benny's ears flattened against his neck as Albert moved. Now I understood why Benny had not defended himself when Albert had put the noose around his neck. He had been taught as a colt to respect a lariat. He had been taught to tie with it and to lead with it. He grew confused and wary only when Albert tightened it and cut off his wind.

Benny, Goldie and I walked slowly along behind Albert, letting him set the pace. Albert refused to say another word though I asked him dozens of questions. I finally gave up and watched him wade slowly through the stream. The mud was beginning to settle and I could see that my favorite spot in Lost Valley, ruined by Albert, would be healed by nature. But no matter how beautiful it became, I knew I would never forget the suffering Benny had endured there.

We were a strange quartet as we wandered past the indifferent cows, down the lane and across the wooden bridge. It seemed to take forever. Whenever the distance between Albert and us was shortened, Benny's ears dropped back in anger. But Benny, still respecting the rope around his neck, made no move to charge

him. For Albert's sake I was glad I was leading Benny
instead of letting him follow free.

As we approached the barn, Mom came out of the
house and walked across the road to Pop and Grandpa
who were sitting on the fence. Their faces showed
their relief and I, too, was beginning to relax a little.
I felt very weary and even Benny, usually so eager to
get to his walnut tree, lagged behind Goldie. Albert
glanced up once but kept walking in a straight line
through the barnyard. Pop jumped from the fence
and started toward Albert but he stopped when he
saw Albert's face. Albert no longer pushed himself
stiffly along: he shuffled, dragging his feet over the
loose stones on the road as though his legs were very
heavy.

Now Benny raised his head and walked a little
faster until his nose touched my knee. He wiggled his
lips affectionately against the coarse threads of my
blue jeans, then gave a shrill whinny at Albert's disap-

pearing back. Albert, far down the road, looked back over his shoulder and I knew that he saw only Benny. Then he turned and was gone.

Questions erupted from Grandpa, Mom and Pop all at once. It took several minutes before the whole story was told. We gave Goldie and Benny a little water and inspected Benny's neck. A little lump had been raised behind his jawbone but there seemed no need to call the veterinarian.

We turned both horses out into the pasture. Benny's first act was to roll his tired body in a dusty spot. He and Goldie then assumed their head-to-tail position under the walnut tree and switched their tails across each other's faces and chests though there were no flies anywhere. Goldie rubbed the side of her face on Benny's haunch in affection and Benny, again the undisputed master, returned her caress with a playful nip on her hind leg. She gave a delighted squeal and we knew that all was right with the world.

"What's going to happen to Albert now?" I asked.

"Well, Norma," Pop said, "he needs psychiatric care, so I guess the thing to do is to tell his mother what happened and let her decide the best course to take."

Pop slipped his arm over my shoulders as we walked back to the house. The weight of it made me realize how drained I was. The thought of crawling between cool sheets in my bed was very appealing—until I thought of the parade which would begin in a couple of hours. I mentioned it and looked from Mom to Pop to Grandpa. They all shook their heads and smiled. Strangely, I wasn't disappointed. Benny and I could make our debut some other time. The only emotion I felt at all was gratitude that Benny was home and unharmed.

Much to my dismay, the Southern Belle did not win first prize. It was announced at half-time that our float took second; first place went to the sophomores. But my classmates and I, as we sat at the game, were proud of our handiwork and some of them felt that first prize would have been ours if Benny had been able to add the finishing, the original, the special touch.

But there were compensations. My friend, Barbara Burek, looking lovely against the background of our southern mansion and moss-draped trees, was crowned Homecoming Queen. Our cheers flooded the football field and eased our disappointment over taking second place with our float.

And when Grand Blanc beat Fenton, the day was complete.

TWELVE

Benny in Training

Not long after Homecoming, Amy and I joined the 4-H club. We were not only intent on learning what we could about the care of our horses but we had our eyes on the 4-H shows scheduled for this summer. The first one showing horses would be in Grand Blanc.

Throughout the winter we studied and worked hard under Mr. Jewett, the 4-H instructor. I learned to add a molasses supplement to Benny's grain to give a sheen to his coat. Since any improvement would be impossible to see in his shaggy old winter coat, I would have to wait for spring to see the results of this feeding.

We were taught to brush a horse's tail from the bottom up; to pull the hairs of the mane and tail away from imbedded burrs instead of trying to slide or pull the burrs out. This knowledge came in handy, because Benny had a gift for finding the thickest patches of burrs and walking through them.

I learned how to clean, saddle-soap and care for all my riding equipment and picked up a good many hints on currying and brushing. And Mr. Jewett taught us such fine points as how to trim the long hairs in the ears and on the fetlocks with the least danger from pointed scissors either to us or the horses.

We studied the conformation points, the differences in breeds of horses, the common illnesses and diseases and how to treat them. The best and surest treatment was, "Call the vet!" We were given the essentials of horse training and shown how to improve good qualities and eliminate or minimize faults and bad habits.

Mr. Jewett was so thorough and patient that Amy and I began to feel like old pros.

Spring announced its arrival with thunderclaps, lightning, hail and torrential rains. Many of the country gravel roads washed out. Rivulets of water gave lawns the desolate look of erosion. Farmers not wise enough to move their stock from pastures in low ground often found themselves out in the rain with their tractors, trying to pull a mooing cow or a frightened pig from the oozing mud. It was so bad that, more often than not, the tractors would also get mired. Day was dark as night, even at noon. Farmers and stock alike could only sit out the flood.

Radios picked up nothing but static and many people were afraid to use their telephones because they believed that lightning traveled along the wires into the earphones and would either deafen or electrocute them.

When the storms' violence was spent, the skies became lighter and the rain settled into a drizzle. The lightning traveled beyond the horizon and the thunder became a distant rumble.

The mud remained for days but the rivers and streams subsided quickly. The grass turned a shining green. Blossoms popped out on fruit trees; gnats, mosquitoes and flies reappeared in their usual hordes and spring brought new life and energy to everything —including old Benny.

The first 4-H show was going to be held soon after school was out. Amy and I met often in the afternoon to practice for our first public appearance. Although we knew that in the actual show we would be competitors, we helped each other with enthusiasm. We wore a dusty oval in the end of the alfalfa field where we practiced equitation. We cantered to the left, we cantered to the right, insisting on the proper lead from Benny and The King. We jogged them tirelessly and walked them impatiently. We executed figure eights, sudden starts into a gallop from a standstill, and sliding stops.

We practiced so much that The King and Benny got stale and we had to slack off for a few days. We used the time to clean and polish all the leather of our gear, rubbing it to a smooth dark finish.

Amy and I had never been to a horse show but Mr. Jewett and Grandpa did their best to tell us what it would be like, what would be expected of us, and what we should work on. When Amy was unable to ride with me, Grandpa drove his car to the alfalfa field and acted alternately as judge and, when his high standards were not met, as trainer.

"When you enter the ring, Norma Jean, let Benny jog along slowly. That's usually the accepted gait to start with. If everyone decided to put his horse into a different gait, you can imagine the confusion there'd be," Grandpa informed me at one of our practice sessions. "Just keep jogging along the rail. Be careful not to get too close to the horse in front of you because you never know how *he* feels about having a horse behind him. And you'd sure hate to stir up a fuss."

I nodded and jogged Benny slowly around the dusty oval, waiting for further instructions from Grandpa who stood thoughtfully in the center of the crude ring, cupping one elbow in his hand. His other hand rested lightly on his whiskered chin. He turned with Benny as Benny made the circle. He looked and sounded like a professional judge.

"Keep your reins loose but don't let them hang so low that you have no control. And just hold them with your left hand, resting your right hand on your leg."

Since I was right-handed, I wondered at this statement but before I could ask, Grandpa gave me the explanation. "That's because when cowboys are roping cattle they use their left hand to rein their horses and their right hand to take their lariats from their saddle horns and make the toss." I nodded and let my right hand fall lightly on my thigh.

"Now canter," said my judge.

Benny changed from his jog into his canter smoothly and we circled the ring a few times before· Grandpa told us to walk.

"Reverse, please," Grandpa said in his most "judgey" voice. I reined Benny around and we proceeded at a walk in the opposite direction from the one we'd been going in.

After that Grandpa had us go through each gait,

one at a time, until finally he said, "Line up your horses, please."

I rode Benny to the center of the ring, faced Grandpa and waited at attention while he looked over each of the invisible horses in the lineup. When he came to a stop in front of Benny, Ben stuck out his nose and nudged Grandpa, begging for a carrot or a lump of sugar. We both burst out laughing. Grandpa was still Grandpa to Ben, no matter how professional his actions. But I got hold of myself as fast as I could and reined Ben's head up, determined to have the proper style for the final judging.

Grandpa walked around Benny, his hand again on his chin. He kept nodding but there was no expression on his face to tell us what he was thinking.

Grandpa walked away from us toward the end of the ring, pretending to make notes on an imaginary pad, then turned and yelled, "We would like to announce the winners of this most difficult class. First prize, the blue ribbon, goes to Norma Cline, riding Benny. Let's all give a big hand for Miss Cline and Benny."

Grandpa clapped and clapped and, laughing, I cantered Ben around the ring once, then accepted my invisible blue ribbon from the judge.

"I think you two will do just fine," he said. "But there are a few things you should work on." Grandpa squatted and stuffed a fresh cut of tobacco into his mouth as I dismounted and sat on the ground beside him. Ben dropped his head and grazed while Grandpa talked.

"Just a couple of things, Norma Jean. You forgot to check Ben's lead when you cantered him. Just look down at his forelegs or shoulders to see which leg he's leading with. If it's the wrong one, then slow him to a trot and get him on the correct lead. One way to do it is to turn his head toward the outside or the ring's fence when you put him into a canter. This forces him to lead out with the proper leg. He was fine going to the right but he was on the wrong lead when you went to the left. Apparently he favors the right lead, so you've got to work on the left more." I nodded that I understood and said that I would.

"When the judge or the announcer asks you to reverse—and it'll almost always be when you're walking or jogging—turn Benny's head toward the inside of the ring. Okay?" I nodded again. "And just one more thing. Something we didn't come across here. If you find you have to pass a horse in the ring, no matter what gait, pass him on the inside. There may be a horse that will canter or jog slower than Ben. You won't want to hamper Benny's natural style by staying behind him, so pass him, on the *inside*, *not* next to the rail. That way you won't be blocking yourself from the judge's view."

Grandpa stood up and walked slowly to his car.

"That's all I can think of right now. You and Amy keep working together until the show. We'll all be there rooting for you."

"Amy and I are the only 4-H members from Grand Blanc who will be showing horses this year," I said.

"Yes, but there'll be plenty of horses from other 4-H clubs, according to Mr. Jewett," Grandpa said. "So you two won't be in strict competition with each other."

"Well, Grandpa, you know and I know and Benny knows that he's the best. But will the judge know?"

We smiled at each other. Grandpa drove off to his little house and Benny and I walked thoughtfully home.

"C'mon outside with me, Norma. I want to show you something."

Pop pushed back his chair from the dinner table and walked out onto the back porch. I glanced at Mom and Howdy, hoping for some clue to Pop's invitation but they merely smiled at each other. Then Howdy shrugged his shoulders at me as if he knew nothing.

I excused myself and walked out to the porch where Pop was waiting. The lilacs were in full bloom and their wonderful scent caught me as I followed Pop down the steps and across the patio toward the front lawn, wondering if I had done something wrong and would be given a talking to.

Pop stopped and pointed toward the barn. My eyes took their direction from his finger.

There, sitting in front of the barn, was a horse trailer.

"Oh, Pop," I said as I caught my breath.

"Let's go take a good look at it," Pop suggested.

Careful inspection showed that the trailer needed a coat of paint and a new roof. Otherwise it was in excellent condition and it was big enough to carry two horses.

"It'll take some work to fix it up but I couldn't pass up the offer. It was delivered today after you'd finished your chores."

"Oh, Pop," I repeated. "It's great. And I won't have to ride Benny into Grand Blanc to the 4-H show. There's even room to take The King, too, if it's okay."

"Of course it's okay. And I have a hunch that once you get the feel of horse shows, this trailer will be getting a lot of use."

Grandpa and I washed and cleaned it thoroughly. We made minor patches and repairs and Grandpa confirmed Pop's opinion that it had a durable and safe frame, springs, and hitch.

It was Grandpa who replaced the old roof with a handsome new one. He put several coats of silver paint on the new roof and on the upper half of the body. The bottom half he painted a true white with green trim.

A few days after the paint had completely dried, I discovered that Grandpa had stenciled a small green insignia on both sides of the trailer, Pop's initials, a large Ⓗ in the style of a western brand. On the left side, down low, just in front of the wheel, he had printed Pop's full name and address.

The rejuvenation was so successful that the trailer looked new. I was going to be proud of hauling Benny to horse shows in such a conveyance.

THIRTEEN

The 4-H Show

B ut on the morning of the 4-H show, we discovered that Benny felt no such pride. He stub-
bornly refused to enter the trailer. He was fine until
he put a forefoot on the tail gate which, when lowered, served as a loading ramp. He backed off instantly
and refused to go one inch closer. I pulled and I
pleaded and I cajoled. Benny simply cocked his ears
and planted his feet firmly against the tug of the lead
strap. Then Grandpa and Pop yelled at him from
behind, waving their arms, hoping to frighten him
into the trailer. Benny moved forward and I walked
up the ramp, thinking he was following. Instead he

stepped over the corner of the ramp and walked to the side of the trailer, pulling me after him.

Would anger work? Grandpa slapped him on his hindquarters, first with the palm of his hand, then smartly with a paddle. Again Benny sidestepped the ramp. He would *not* walk up it.

Would Goldie help? She was led from the barnyard, whinnying plaintively, knowing that Benny was going to leave her. Grandpa led her past Benny, up the ramp and into the trailer. He secured her and let himself out through the little side door at the front of the trailer, thinking that Benny might feel inclined to follow her. Benny reached out with one forefoot, touched the tip of his iron shoe to the ramp and hastily took it off.

"Sure you don't want to show Goldie instead, Norma?" Pop and Grandpa joked. It was an effort to smile. Benny's ornery behavior was unnerving me further. I had a bad case of "stage fright" as it was, just thinking about the horse show.

"Well, I have an idea," said Grandpa. I relaxed my pull on Benny's lead strap, eager for any suggestions.

Grandpa disappeared into the barn for a few moments and returned with the same long rope Albert Foster had used on Benny last year. Benny had no fear of the rope itself but he watched Grandpa and

Pop warily as they approached him, one from each side, each holding an end of the rope. Benny flinched when the rough rope touched his hindquarters but held his ground until Pop and Grandpa reached the sides of the trailer when they both pulled hard. Benny leaned against the rope, almost sitting on his haunches. His eyes looked from one to the other, then to me, wondering how two people who were standing almost in front of him could be exerting so much pressure from behind. He stepped forward, regaining his normal posture, but when the pressure of the rope was applied again, he gave a loud sigh and walked into the trailer beside Goldie.

His change of heart surprised me so much that he almost walked over me. Knowing how unpredictable old Ben could sometimes be, I backed Goldie out immediately and we fastened the tail gate.

I climbed into the back seat of the car, feeling tired already. I was wedged in with the shining saddle and bridle and all the other paraphernalia so important for Ben's debut, leaving room for Amy and her gear. Pop drove and Grandpa rode in front with him. We arrived at Amy's house on schedule.

The King reacted to the trailer in much the same way Ben had. But we knew how to handle that kind of behavior now. With Amy's dad on one end of the rope, Pop on the other, and Benny in the trailer, The

King surrendered with very little struggle and walked up the ramp into the trailer.

Amy and I had no desire to talk. We only exchanged glances now and then, showing that it took all our concentration to cope with our nervousness. The trailer jerked the car a little as we hit bumps in the gravel road. Amy and I swiveled our heads around every few seconds to make sure the trailer was still with us. Amy's dad had joined Pop and Grandpa in the front seat and they talked continuously, teasing us about our silence.

When we drove into the school yard, I was surprised at the changes. Tents had been erected to house cages of prize chickens, rabbits, and other stock. The bus shed had been converted into stalls for cattle and calves. We drove at five miles an hour to keep from running over all the children, parents, teachers and an occasional loose animal being wildly chased by its owner. The far end of the bus shed had been partitioned off into standing stalls for the horses.

When we reached it, riders from other schools had already arrived and a few more horse trailers were pulling into the school yard behind us. We climbed out of the car and stood for a few minutes to get our bearings. Mr. Bentley suggested that we find our stalls first, so that when we unloaded our horses, we'd know exactly where to take them.

Amy and I peered into the trailer through the little door in front to make sure Benny and The King were all right. Benny whinnied his usual hello at me, stretching his muzzle toward me for a lump of sugar. I rewarded him with two lumps and a pat on the nose; Amy fed The King a long carrot. Both had behaved well and were fairly calm though they were very aware of the strange noises outside the trailer. Their eyes kept rolling backwards, trying to see out the opening above the tail gate. The King appeared to be a little skittish but we knew that he would be manageable as long as Benny was near him.

Then Amy and I raced over to the rows of makeshift horse stalls and read the placards with the name of the owner, the horse and the 4-H club tacked on the posts of every stall. We found our stalls just inside the third row: Benny was assigned to an end stall; The King was next to him. We hurried back to the trailer, anxious to get the horses and ourselves comfortable so that we could inspect the competition.

Both horses backed out of the trailer without any fuss. Benny tossed his head and whinnied a loud notice of his arrival. There were several responses. To these both Benny and The King replied. From then on for as long as we were around, whinnies were exchanged again and again with every horse.

Grandpa, Pop and Mr. Bentley drove off to find a

spot at the end of the football field to unhitch and park the trailer. Amy and I, meanwhile, were busy securing our two curious horses in their stalls. Not forgetting how unwise it would be to tie Benny only by his halter, I slipped a noose around his neck and fastened it to the headboard. There was no doubt that Benny would respect that rope no matter how inclined he might be to ignore the lead strap on his halter. I left some slack in the rope so that he could back up a few feet but not enough to let him move over to bother The King.

I was very thankful that The King was next to Benny. I didn't want Ben giving a strange horse any of those little nips he gave Goldie. A strange horse might nip or even kick back. The King and Benny had a great deal of respect for each other, so there was no worry on that score.

Amy and I arranged our riding equipment on wooden sawhorses provided for the purpose. We brought water to the horses. Benny drank most of it, so that I had to make a second trip. We fed them each a little grain and talked to them to help them acclimate themselves to this strange place and in the process, perhaps, quell some of our own anxieties.

"Amy?"

"What?"

"Are you nervous?"

"No," she lied, "are you?"

"No," I lied back.

Amy stepped from The King's side, leaned against a bale of straw and said, "Norma."

"What?"

"Yes, I am, too."

"Me, too."

At that moment Pop, Grandpa, and Mr. Bentley walked in and found us laughing so hard we had to wipe away the tears.

"What's so funny, girls?" asked Mr. Bentley. He sat on a dusty bale of straw and wiped his bald spot and throat with a big polka dot handkerchief.

"Oh, nothing, really." Amy giggled. "I guess we're just laughing at ourselves."

"It looks to me as though you two have things pretty well squared away," said Pop. "There's plenty of time before you'll be showing, so I guess Mr. Bentley and I will head for home. I know you'll be doing a lot of wandering around. We'll just go hurry up your mothers and be back before the show starts."

"Is there anything you girls need?" Mr. Bentley asked.

"No, thank you," we answered together.

"I'm going to stay with the girls," said Grandpa. "There's a lot here I've got to look over too. Mainly the other horses. Want to see what I can do to eliminate the competition. Like a burr under someone's saddle or something."

We all laughed together. I was glad Grandpa was staying around. His jokes and his constant good humor never failed to drive away the worries or the blues. I took a deep breath. I was almost ready to face the competition.

"Well, we'll be off," Pop said. "You girls take good care of Grandpa and the horses. Don't let any of them get loose." Grandpa chuckled.

"I guess now's as good a time as any to see what we're up against," he said. "Might as well see what old plugs are entered against our two champs."

"And after that, we can make the rounds of the other animals and the exhibits," I said.

We began our walk down the first aisle of stalls. We did this methodically, not wanting to miss a single horse. We read each placard and analyzed the good and bad points of every horse. We stole several looks at the owner, if he happened to be standing near his horse, and his riding equipment. Most of the exhibitors were extremely friendly. They smiled, nodded, or said hello as we passed. It was obvious to them that we were 4-H members and would also be riding in the show.

Some stalls were empty. It must be that more horses

were due to arrive, that they were being walked or ridden around the school yard, or that there were more stalls than horses. Most of the exhibitors brought their own straw for bedding but the Grand Blanc 4-H club had provided some extra for those who might need it.

The horses were of all breeds, ages, and conditions. A roan mare with a beautiful dish-faced head and sloping shoulders watched us pass. As we did, she turned slightly and we noticed a nasty gash down her hindquarters from her flank almost to her hock. It was covered with a green ointment which attracted flies. The mare stamped her foot constantly trying to get rid of them.

"Looks like she got tangled in some barbed wire," Grandpa remarked.

"That looks awful. Do you think it hurts much?" I asked.

"No, the cut doesn't look deep but her skin probably feels pretty tight. The flies are bothering her more than anything."

"Can she be shown like that?" Amy asked.

"Apparently she can," Grandpa said. "It looks like a recent cut and her owner seems to be doing what he can for it. I imagine the judge will try to do the best he can by her."

"She's a nice mare," I said.

Amy drew our attention to the end stall. Two standing stalls had been arranged to make one box stall. Inside, the beautiful white and gold of a horse's coat shone like the morning sun.

"Wow!" Amy whispered to me. "Look at that Palomino."

The golden stallion was tied to the far side of the stall. He tossed his head as we walked to the rails. His forelock fell over his big brown eyes and his thick mane, as white as fresh milk, rippled along his neck. The end of his tail fanned out on top of the bedding and the gold of his shining body made the yellow straw look pale and dull. He warned us with his eyes and ears not to go any nearer.

A boy of about fifteen sat on an old milking stool at one corner of the stall, chewing on a piece of straw. His blond hair tumbled loosely around his ears. He wore stiff blue jeans, faded with wear, and watched us proudly as we admired the stallion.

"Is she yours?" Grandpa asked him.

"No, sir, he belongs to my dad."

"Are you going to show him?" I asked.

"No. He's just on exhibition. Dad's going to take him around to some of the shows this summer to let people see how nice a horse he is. He's sort of advertising him for stud service."

We chatted for a few moments longer and agreed on his merits and his beauty. As we walked away, Amy and I looked at each other with relief. Neither of us wanted to show against competition like that.

"Even if you did," Grandpa said, "you'd probably win. He's a pretty animal, sure, but his disposition isn't suited to a member of the 4-H. Besides, he's very touchy. That's why they have him off in a corner of that big box stall."

We nodded but were still relieved. We looked at the rest of the horses—the bays, chestnuts, pintos, two albinos and one Appaloosa mare. We picked out the Quarter Horses, the Arabians and the mixed breeds. We rubbed our hands along the saddles, checking the condition of the leather. We patted The King and Benny as we walked by them and around into the next aisle. We talked to several 4-H members and their parents, complimenting them on their horses, feeling that, so far, Benny and The King had no serious competition. We knew, though, that many of these horses were in top condition and had been given as much care and love as ours had. We knew we'd have to be on our toes. And I was certain of one fact: there was not one horse older than Benny. But I couldn't decide whether or not this was an advantage.

The three of us spent the next hour wandering over the school grounds, looking at the other exhibits.

FOURTEEN

The Winners

They were judging the sheep when we arrived in that tent but we quickly tired of it. We loved the lambs but the ewes all looked alike. They were cleaner than usual but their insistent bleating drove us away in search of a hot dog stand where we could have lunch.

After lunch we looked at the various breeds of cattle, admiring the way their owners had curled the wiry hair along the flanks of the Herefords and the black Aberdeen Angus. The Angus were beautiful animals —beefy, short, hornless, and round. They seemed to have no necks: their heads grew right out of their shoulders.

We walked as quickly as we could through the tent where the chickens were caged, wrinkling our noses at the unpleasant odor, and made for the tent where there were pigs of all kinds—bristly pigs, black and white, all white and spotted pigs, some with piglets so young they looked like small rats. There were even a few heavy grunting boars with ridiculous corkscrew tails.

We scanned the entries in the sewing, flower, and vegetable exhibits, and the prize foods from the home economic classes. First and second place winners wore their ribbons pinned to straw hats or on their proud chests but those who took the yellow, white, green, and other ribbons—third, fourth, and fifth prizes and on down—weren't quite so eager to flaunt them and usually attached them to animal and poultry pens or to whatever had taken the prize.

By this time Amy and I were tired of exhibits. We went back to the shed and its still whinnying horses in plenty of time to relax before our class was called to the ring.

Mom, Pop and the Bentleys arrived as we were grooming Benny and The King. Grandpa watched comfortably from a bale of straw, leaning his back against a splintery post. He was chewing his tobacco and looking very, very proud.

"Getting ready so soon, girls?" Mr. Bentley asked.

"Yes," Amy answered, "because we want to get everything done now so we can ride around a little bit and get the horses used to the noise and the crowds."

"Sounds like a good idea," Pop said.

Benny and The King seemed remarkably calm in their unfamiliar surroundings but Benny's insatiable curiosity would not allow him to relax. He whinnied often in response to all kinds of new noises as well as to other whinnies, snorts, and nickers. His eyes moved up, down, and around continuously. He was going to be sure not to miss anything. Though he seemed not to be paying any attention to me, he obeyed each of my orders instantly, almost unconsciously. "Move over, Ben." "Back up." "Step up, Benny." "Now hold still." Each command was carried out so punctiliously and automatically I began to wonder if he would have taken orders from anyone, until Amy tried to retrieve a bracelet she dropped in the straw between his forelegs. She pushed against him gently and told him to move. Ben looked at her absently, ignoring her request, until he heard the same command in my voice.

We saddled the horses and mounted, thanking our families for their good wishes. Each in his own way had given Amy and me confidence.

Grandpa whispered, "The King is no competition for Benny and neither is any other horse around here."

We walked out into the noise of people and animals. Other riders were getting ready to mount or were moving toward the ring. The scattered crowds began drifting toward it, too.

Benny caught the excitement and refused to walk. He jogged excitedly. I patted his neck and talked to him as much for my own benefit as for his, until we heard over the public address system, "All exhibitors for Class Number Fourteen, Pleasure Riding, please enter the ring to your right!"

My hands shook a little, and Benny, aware of my nervousness, kept up his jog.

Amy entered the ring just ahead of me, following two other horses. We jogged along the rail and I scanned the audience in the stands for Mom, Pop and

Grandpa. By the time we had made the full circle, I saw that Grandpa had worked his way to the front with Mom and Pop. They waved to me and my nervousness dropped away. I could feel Benny relax. He arched his neck proudly, as eager to please as I was.

The ring seemed suddenly full of horses. I hadn't realized so many of them had been stabled in the bus shed. As we continued jogging, they began to spread out in a line so that I could count them. There were about eighteen, all obviously much younger than Ben. For some reason, that fired my spirit: I became absolutely determined to show the very lean judge in the white Stetson, sunglasses, and cowboy boots that he might have trouble picking his second and third choices but Benny was going to be his first.

"Canter, please," blared the loudspeaker.

I turned Benny's head to the rail and tightened my knees. Benny shifted his weight and we were rocking along smoothly in his slow canter. We passed another pinto—on the inside; I remembered Grandpa's instructions. The rider was having difficulty keeping control of him. The pinto was straining at the bit, eager to run. I forgot him as soon as we were by and glanced at the center of the ring. The judge was standing with his back to my side of the ring! He hadn't even noticed Benny! But he had noticed Amy and The King. In fact, the judge was studying the fine action of The King's muscular legs.

Benny's ears were all the way forward. His spotted body glistened in the sunlight. (This time the bath had been a complete and quiet success.) His short legs raised and lowered themselves neatly on the dusty ground. My back was straight but relaxed. And Benny was proud and alive and magnificent!

"Walk, please."

A very slight pull on the reins brought Benny's speed down but he would not walk! His jog was smooth and made it easy for me to keep a flat seat. But walk he would not, though his jog was slower than the walk of some of the other horses. Out of the corner of my eye I saw that the judge was looking in my direction but with his dark glasses it was difficult to tell whether he was looking at Benny and me. I crossed the fingers of my right hand, out of sight of the judge, until we were ordered to "Jog or trot, please."

I let the reins out a little and Benny speeded up his jog. I was glad to be out of the walking gait. Amy and I exchanged glances across the ring and smiled at each other. The judge seemed to be looking everywhere but at Benny.

"Reverse, please."

The horses were beginning to get warm: white lather was showing around the saddle girths of some of them. I glanced down and saw that Benny was turning a little darker with sweat but not yet lathering. Again, at the judge's command, we maneuvered our mounts through the three gaits. Benny still refused to walk. I tightened up on the reins more than I ever had, hoping to slow him down to a point where he would have no choice but to walk. But the unaccustomed pressure of the bit bothered him and he tossed his head in protest. What could I do but let him jog?

The King appeared to be at his best. He held his head erect; his black mane flowed in the breeze. Amy looked delighted, as well she might. Her plaid cotton shirt complemented the shine of her brown western saddle. She held her booted feet correctly in the wooden stirrups and I admitted, with a little envy, that she was turning into a very accomplished rider. Her arms held the reins loosely and The King performed for the judge.

When we were instructed to line our horses up in the center of the ring, Amy and I managed to get beside each other near one end. We waited anxiously for the judge to finish his general inspection as he walked up the front and down the back of the line. Then he began his more careful inspection of each horse, beginning at the other end from us, examining the tack and asking each rider to back his horse up. When the judge reached The King, he ran his hand lightly over The King's ribs, then nodded at Amy to back him. Amy pulled on the reins and tightened her knee-grip; The King tucked in his chin and stepped back a few feet. Amy resumed her position beside me.

I heard the judge say to her, "I can see that you've taken good care of your horse. He does sweat a little too easily, though, which might mean that he either doesn't get enough exercise or that you're feeding him a little too much. One other little thing I might mention. You see how the bit wrinkles the corners of his mouth?" Amy leaned forward and said, "Yes, sir." "You might loosen each cheek strap just a notch. It looks as though your horse has a pretty sensitive mouth and the bit ought to fit a little more comfortably."

Amy thanked him and as he glanced at the number on her arm, he scratched a few notes on his clipboard and stepped over in front of Benny.

Benny said hello with his raspy "huh, huh, huh," and stuck his nose out for a tidbit before I could stop him. The judge gave him a broad smile: the judge was much younger than he looked from a distance. He tucked his clipboard under his arm and separated Benny's lips to look at his teeth. He nodded and I tugged on the reins to back Benny up. I felt Ben's resistance but he did step back. The judge patted Benny on his flank and said, "I think you're pretty kind to your horse, too. He's a little on the fat side.

It's not necessary to feed him quite so much in the hot weather, you know. He does have a nice coat, though. How old is he?"

"He's over twenty, sir."

"Do you ride him often?"

"Nearly every day."

"How's his wind?"

"Getting short but it's not too bad yet."

"H-m-m-m-m." He moved on to the roan mare with the wound and questioned the rider about her. Grandpa was right. It was from barbed wire but I had difficulty listening to the conversation because I was so occupied wondering what the judge's questions about Benny's wind and age meant. Were they good or bad? Did I give the right answers?

The judge finished his questioning and walked back to the officials' booth. A voice blared over the loud-speaker, "Will the following horses and riders please take to the rail. If your number is not called, please remain where you are in the center of the ring."

Seven numbers were called, Amy's among them, but not mine. Disappointment dug at my throat. The best horses had been called out so the judge could decide among them for first and second places. The horses were put through their gaits and I crossed my fingers, this time for Amy and The King. They lined up once more at the end of the row. We could hardly wait for the results to be announced.

"Ladies and gentlemen, I am very proud to announce the winners of this fine class, Class Number Fourteen, Pleasure Riding." The speaker cleared his throat. "First prize, the blue ribbon, goes to . . ." I swallowed hard and held my breath. ". . . Miss Norma Cline from Grand Blanc, riding Benny!"

I felt weak all over and wasn't at all sure I had heard correctly. But the audience was clapping: the loudest claps came from where my family was standing. The riders next to me were looking at Benny, unable to conceal their own disappointment but applauding just the same.

Benny stepped out without waiting for a signal from me. He had heard his name clearly enough. He walked—not jogged—up to the judge and through a haze I saw the judge fasten the blue ribbon to Benny's bridle.

"Canter once around the ring for the audience," he said, smiling at me.

The applause continued. Mom, Pop and Grandpa cheered when I rode past them. I stopped just outside the gate and turned to face the ring to see how Amy and The King fared. Second, third, fourth and fifth places were announced—all from other school districts. Then I heard Amy's name over the loudspeaker: she had won sixth prize. The rest of the horses trudged out.

"Norma, I'm so happy for you," Amy said as she came through the gate where I was waiting for her.

"Oh, thank you, Amy, I'm so proud of Benny—and of you and The King. We did take two prizes."

"I have to admit I'm a little jealous, Norma," Amy said, "but out of eighteen horses, even a sixth place isn't too bad."

We rode back to our stalls where we knew our families would be waiting for us.

"Oh, we're proud of you girls!"

"You both did wonderfully well."

"Norma, Benny's a wonder!"

"Amy, you and The King will do even better in the next show."

Everybody talked at once and it was several minutes before we calmed down enough to have rational conversation. Amy stood leaning against The King's warm shoulder while I held Benny's head in my arm. We were both very proud of our horses.

"Well, that certainly was exciting," I said. "When can we do it again?" Everyone laughed. Grandpa said, "No one's prouder than I am of my granddaughter and a plug that's older than me." That made us all laugh harder.

FIFTEEN

Grandpa

I'm certainly not complaining," I told Amy, after the excitement was over, "but why do you suppose, out of all those eighteen horses, Benny was chosen for first place?" I asked.

"Because he was one of the best," Pop answered.

"But Benny did some things wrong in the ring. He didn't really want to back up and I couldn't get him to walk. Most of the other horses did everything perfectly."

"I imagine," Mr. Bentley said, "the judge based his decision on many different things. He considered the condition of the horses and equipment, the kind of care they've had, the riding ability of each rider, the manners and behavior of the horses—lots of things. All the horses had some faults, Norma. It's just that the judge felt that Benny had the fewest."

"It was a good class, I think," Amy said sincerely. "Of course, I'd like to have won, too, but I don't feel the judge placed me unfairly. The King was good but so were the others. And the judge is right about one thing, The King *is* too fat!"

Amy and I talked excitedly about showing Benny and The King again while our parents exchanged glances. Suddenly we heard a moan. I turned and saw Grandpa slump on a bale of straw, clutching his chest.

Pop was the first to reach him. He sat beside him and put his arm around Grandpa's shoulders, trying to make him comfortable. Grandpa's face was ashen and his breathing was labored. Nobody spoke. We knew that Grandpa was very ill.

"We'd better get him to the hospital right away," Pop said.

"Please take my car," Mr. Bentley said. "I'll stay here and help the girls get the horses home."

"No, I'll go with you," I said to Mom and Pop.

"I'll go, too," Amy said.

"There'll be nothing for you to do right now,

Norma. You and Amy go home and take care of your horses. Grandpa will be all right but we must get him to the hospital right away. You go along home and we'll call you from the hospital."

"All right. I will. But please, please call me as soon as you can."

I felt like crying but I wanted to be brave. Grandpa's eyes were closed and I would have thought he had fallen asleep except for his heavy breathing. I leaned over and kissed him on the cheek. He smiled but didn't open his eyes.

"I hope you'll feel better soon, Grandpa," I said, feeling it was a very inadequate way of saying what I hoped for him.

Grandpa was indeed very sick. He never left the hospital. He lay many weeks in a little white room, showing such great improvement at first that we thought he might recover. Then suddenly his strength ebbed and for several weeks he was in an oxygen tent. He was unconscious his last few days, unaware of any of his worried and loving visitors.

Pop called us at home in the middle of the night from the hospital to tell us that Grandpa had gone. Earl, Howdy and I sat in the living room and cried until dawn when Mom and Pop brought Susie home with them.

It wasn't long before I found myself in Benny's stall, my arms tight around his neck, my face buried in his bristly mane. Benny stood relaxed and rubbed his nose comfortingly against my side. I cried a long time, but finally it was over. I slid to the soft straw beside Benny's forelegs and rested my forehead against Benny's bony knee. Benny's lips caressed the top of my head.

It seemed unfair that Grandpa should be taken from us. He was indispensable to the farm and to our lives. He'd taught us all a good share of what we knew about living. But, sitting there in the warm straw beside Benny, I realized that Grandpa would always be with us; he could never be forgotten.

Benny was a great comfort to me in the next few months until the pain I felt at the loss of Grandpa began healing. Benny himself seemed younger, some-how, and more active, yet he was never better be-haved. Never once did he take advantage of my grief by disobeying me or playing tricks on me. And Goldie's disposition improved markedly. Benny must have lectured her.

Being Benny, he sensed our loss. And of course he missed Grandpa, too. I guessed how much when I was awakened many mornings by a long plaintive whinny. It was always at sunrise, at the time when Grandpa's car would have been bouncing across the fields to the barn for the morning chores. Benny gave the same mournful whinny at unpredictable times while I was riding him in the next several weeks: he would raise his nose skyward and let out a whinny that was different from any others I had ever heard, or would ever hear again.

SIXTEEN

Struggle for Life

I wished that Grandpa could have been with us when Benny won a first place blue ribbon, a trophy in the western pleasure class, and a second place in equitation at the Fenton Horse Show.

I wished that he had seen Benny win another red ribbon at Columbiaville when he competed against two Arabian stallions, several purebred Quarter Horses, and many others just as fine.

I know what special pride he would have felt to see Benny win over a marvelous Morgan mare in a special class for horses fifteen years and older at the Holly Horse Show. The judge had such a difficult time deciding between Benny and the Morgan for first and second places that he dismissed the rest of the class from the ring to concentrate on these two.

Benny became almost a professional show horse that year. He loved competition whether in the show ring or racing other horses on country roads near the farm. The response of an audience stimulated him so much that his steps grew flashier and his tail switched with determination to be top horse. He invariably drew the hearts of the people and the eyes of the judges to him. There were many times when he placed very low or not at all but he was never disappointed, never disheartened. He had the spirit of a wonderful show-off and a true competitor.

The following spring we retired Benny from show business, though it was hard to accept the fact that he no longer needed, or should have, the amount of work, exercise and play he'd been getting. According to my calculations, Benny was almost twenty-five years old. Multiplying that by three meant that Benny had reached the human age of seventy-five! No wonder his wind was shorter (it had never been too good to begin with), his speed slower, and his legs a little weaker. The daily rides grew considerably shorter but the talks, very much longer.

But his senses were strong and responsive: his eyes, still alert and clear; his hearing, perfect. His whinny was loud and young; his mind receptive, and his heartbeat as steady as ever. Should he be retired to pasture permanently? Should I let him live out his remaining years in undisturbed comfort? Perhaps I should spend my riding time on the younger Goldie? Benny answered these questions himself just three weeks after he went into involuntary retirement.

Goldie was pleasant to ride. She was obedient. In fact she was so obedient there was no challenge in it. She never tossed her head when I refused to let her run or fought the bit when we galloped. She never startled me by kicking her heels in the air just because it was a beautiful spring day or a robin had suddenly appeared. She never shied because a rabbit or a chipmunk hopped out onto the road. She behaved exactly as she was told. She was willing and her gaits were good. Expert horsemen would have called her a well-trained, perfectly mannered horse. She was.

But compared to Ben, riding Goldie was like riding a rocking horse. He was all fire and spirit, independence and stubbornness, eagerness, shrewdness and joy. Riding Ben was exhilaration; riding Goldie was like being on a carousel—fun for a short time.

Ben often disagreed with me, became angry with me, refused to obey me. He was more often right than not. He never kicked at me, never actually bit me, though he threatened to once in a while and I believe now that it was more to discipline me, to keep me in line, than to be cantankerous.

He was the boss, not I. On the contrary, I was his slave: I cleaned his stall, I brushed and curried him, I fed him, I polished his equipment. And though he was tyrannical with Goldie, he never was with me.

But he was wise and the years added to his wisdom —so wise that our respect ripened into devotion.

The Michigan spring rolled around as it usually does with a little slushy snow, some rain, a little sunshine. Here and there, some green showed on the tips of bushes and trees and the birds were back again, singing out the last patches of winter. Cold days alternated with breathtakingly clear warm ones.

It was on one of the warm ones when I had had Goldie out for a long ride with Amy and The King that we returned to the barn just before dusk, tired and hungry. Goldie's belly and legs were coated with mud. The spring sunshine had not had time to dry out roads and fields. Goldie's hooves squished across the barnyard and as I dismounted, I noticed that Benny was not standing under the walnut tree, watching for our return. I concluded that he had gone farther out in the pasture in search of some of the new grass that was just beginning to sprout in the dampest spots. I rubbed Goldie down, walked her to cool her, and prepared the stalls for the night. Goldie whinnied for Benny, received no reply, and buried her nose in her oats. Benny still hadn't returned after I had turned the electric pump on to fill the water trough for the cattle, so I picked my way through the mud in the barnyard around to the back of the barn.

"B-e-n-n-y," I hollered. *"Ben-eee!"*

He had always been good about responding to my call whether it was feeding time or not. If he didn't feel like trotting up to the barn, he would whinny an answer to let me know where he was so that I could walk down to him, slip his bridle on, and ride him back. There was no answer and I was suddenly afraid that he might have been stolen again. I shivered, even though the air was still warm. I pushed that thought from my mind, deciding that Ben was probably angry with me for leaving him home alone and was punishing me.

Trudging through acres of mud before I could find that stubborn animal might take hours. I resolutely tramped back to the barn and interrupted Goldie's hay-munching by slipping the bridle over her ears. Riding her was obviously the quickest and most sensible way of looking for Ben.

The barn and the trees now cast long shadows. My stomach grumbled with hunger and I felt annoyed at Benny's impertinence in not answering my call. He was getting more ornery than ever in retirement.

Goldie's swift Tennessee walk covered the pasture quickly but nowhere could we find a sign of Benny. We slipped down the hill in the farthest pasture toward the muddy creek to cross the bridge. The tangled bushes on the other side were bare but so thick and high that they seemed impenetrable except for a few paths here and there made by the cattle and horses and used by an occasional deer. The black muck in that low ground was often treacherous this time of year but it was the only place left to look. I stopped in the middle of the bridge for a moment to let Goldie get her wind before attacking the prickly bushes. Though the creek had only a few inches of water, the banks were like a saturated sponge.

A few yards up the creek was a big mound of very wet mud, black and brown. I knew by the size of it, it had to be an animal—a deer, a steer, or a horse! There were no signs of movement and I was afraid it was dead.

"Please, God, don't let it be Benny," I prayed.

I kept praying silently as I turned Goldie around and hurried her back into the pasture. I jumped off and fastened her reins to the nearest fence post and walked, my heart pounding in my ears, to the sloping bank of the creek.

I stopped where the wet pasture turned into muck

and gazing down at the motionless animal, I recognized Benny. He was on his side, completely covered with slime, so that not one grey-white hair showed. His hooves were under the few inches of water in the creek but his legs and body were out of it, on the bank. The mud around him was broken and little pools of dirty water seeped up where his legs had punctured through the spongy ground. He had fought the muck, trying desperately to get out.

Suddenly, there was a loud grunt and Benny raised his head and looked over his shoulder at me! He swung his head forward again, pushed his chin against the mud for leverage, and tried to stand. But his legs sank immediately into the sucking ground. He pulled them out and tried again. He thrashed violently, trying to find something solid to get his hooves on. Each time he'd get his legs under him, they would sink with a squish. He could pull them free only by letting his weight fall sideways onto the bank.

Startled and alarmed by the vehemence of his fight to get free, my crying stopped abruptly and I tried to think what to do next. I talked soothingly to him. In addition to all the other dangers, there was the chance that he might break a leg in the grasping muck.

As Ben sank back on his side, this time with a hopeless sigh, I found my legs and sprinted for Goldie. I leapt onto her back and whipped my heels into her sides. She took off, galloping full speed for the barn.

We were reckless. Goldie slipped often and came close to falling but miraculously we slid to a standing stop under the walnut tree. I pushed myself from Goldie's back to the fence, swung myself over it and ran across the road without looking right or left for oncoming cars.

Mom gave me an angry look as I banged the kitchen door shut against the wall and tracked mud all over the floor. But her expression changed to fear as I blurted out my story.

Earl, who was spending a weekend home from college, Howdy and Pop pulled on their boots while Mom called Mr. King, our neighbor, to ask if he would help us with his tractor.

We raced to the barn to wait for Mr. King. While I put Goldie in her stall to keep her out of the way, Earl chased the cattle from the big gate so that Mr. King could drive his tractor through it. As soon as he arrived we hopped on the back of it, drove in silence down the hill and through the pastures to the creek. Mr. King drove the tractor as close to the edge as he could without getting mired. I jumped off and ran to the edge of the bank. Benny was breathing with difficulty; his brown eyes had filmed over. He was obviously exhausted.

"Please, Benny, lie quietly. I don't want you to wear yourself out," I pleaded. Ben cocked his mud-caked ear toward me but otherwise made no movement.

"We'll have to figure the best way to get him out of there," Mr. King said. "I can't get the tractor any closer or we'll defeat our whole purpose by getting that stuck too."

"But we've got to do something!" I cried. "Benny might kill himself trying. What can we do?"

"Well, we can try getting a sling around his belly and dragging him out with the tractor. That might be a little hard to do, though, because a couple of us will have to take our chances with those flailing hooves when Benny starts another struggle. If he doesn't struggle, then the problem will be to get the sling around under him. He's pretty slick all over with mud."

Instead of working himself closer to the edge of the slippery bank where he might have got a foothold, Benny, in his last frantic attempts to escape, had wriggled near the center of the creek where the muck was worst. I remembered stories about three or four animals who had been trapped in the muck of this creek on other farms. Those who didn't get help died within a few hours. They mired themselves more and more deeply into the muck so that their nostrils and mouths clogged and they either suffocated or drowned. We *couldn't* let that happen to Benny!

Benny raised his head and struggled once again. We

all talked to him, trying to quiet him, trying to relax him, trying to make him understand that the wisest course was to be still. When he quit thrashing he was still nearer the center of the creek so that when he rested his head on the mud, his nose was only a few inches from the turbid water.

Earl and Howdy dropped to their stomachs, each holding an end of the sling and slithered down the bank toward Benny like awkward snakes. He raised his head a little and watched them approach but made no move. With their foreheads resting on Benny's backbone, the boys dropped one end of the sling over his side. Then Earl raised himself slowly to his knees. He was trying to reach around Benny and push the far end of the sling as far under Benny as possible. But as soon as Earl put his weight on his knees, he sank to his waist in the mud.

"Don't get excited and stir Ben up again," Pop said. "We don't want him to wriggle around on top of Earl while he's stuck!"

"Pat him, Howdy, talk to him," I said. Howdy's muddy hand stroked Benny's free shoulder and though I could see Howdy's lips moving, I couldn't hear what he was saying.

Pop and Mr. King, both now on their stomachs, slid cautiously down the bank until they could reach Earl. They grasped him under both arms, pulled backwards and crawled inch by slippery inch, feet first, up the bank until Earl's legs were free and he was lying on his back. Working his arms like flippers, Earl was able to propel himself the rest of the way up the bank to more solid ground. Then he and the men leaned down the bank and gave Howdy, who also was wedged in the mud, a final pull up.

"There's no way I can see that we can get that sling under Benny's middle," Earl said.

"Earl's right," Howdy said. "You saw what just happened. We'll have to think of something else."

"There's only one other way," Mr. King said. "It's pretty dangerous but it's sure he can't get himself out of there alone." He walked over to the tractor and returned with a coil of heavy manila rope. I looked at him questioningly and he explained, "We'll just have to put the rope around Benny's neck and try to pull him out."

I swallowed hard. "I can see how dangerous it is. There's a chance that if he's mired very deep and the pull of the rope doesn't free him, his neck might get broken."

Mr. King nodded. Then I happened to think of something.

"I'm afraid he'll try to fight it instead of working with it," I said. "Remember when Albert Foster stole him? Remember how he mistreated Benny with that tight noose around his neck? Remember how it confused him and made him afraid? What if he does that now? What if he gets frightened? He might choke to death or his neck might be snapped."

"Norma," Pop said. He rested both hands on my shoulders and leaned over a little to see me closely in the near dark. "Benny can't get out alone. We can't get a sling around him. There is simply no other way. We've got to try it."

I glanced at Benny lying in his muddy grave, then I looked down at my boots and nodded.

Mr. King slid carefully down the bank and tied the rope-around Ben's neck. Ben did not resist. His breathing was still raspy and his eyes were half closed. Mr. King crawled away from Benny and walked to the tractor where he tied the other end of the rope to the drawbar.

"I didn't make a slipknot, Norma, so it won't get any tighter around his neck than it already is. I do want to warn you, though, that it might choke him a little because of the angle of his body to the direction I have to drive the tractor in. I promise you I'll be very careful and if it looks as though it's going badly, I'll stop."

He climbed up on the metal seat.

"Howard, you and the boys watch closely," Mr. King called. "I can't see Benny from here but you let me know the instant you want me to stop, back up, or go forward."

Benny hadn't struggled much in the past few minutes. I was very much afraid that he was completely worn out and incapable of any struggle. If he couldn't help himself and Mr. King by pulling against the rope, I knew it would be hopeless.

The tractor roared when Mr. King turned on the ignition but it feathered down when he shifted into low and started forward. My breath stopped and my eyes fastened on Benny's head and neck. I watched the rope skip as the tractor took up the slack. When it was nearly taut, Mr. King stopped the tractor. He got off, went back for one last look at the rope and the angle of Benny's neck, and silently climbed back onto the tractor. Pop motioned him slowly ahead.

I squatted at the edge of the bank where in the quickly fading light I could see Benny's face. I talked to him nonsensically, hoping to cajole him into one more try. Ben's eyes were still heavy and his breathing painfully labored but he twitched an ear toward me at the sound of my voice. He made no other response. At least he wasn't unconscious yet.

As the rope began pulling on Benny, I sucked in my breath. The rope was so heavy it made ruts in the mud plastered on his neck. As it tightened on his windpipe, Benny's eyes rolled back and his nostrils flared. He was gasping for air, his head and neck twisted against the rope. He made no effort to move his body or his legs.

"Stop!" I yelled. "He's not going to try. He's too old. He's frightened. He's worn out. Maybe he's dying! Please stop! We can't do it this way."

The rope slackened immediately and Benny's nose came to rest again on the black muck. Now his eyes were completely closed. I peered anxiously at him and saw that he was still breathing. I thought I could hear his heart pounding rapidly but it was my own.

"Norma, don't let him give up! And don't *you* give up either!" Suddenly I seemed to hear Grandpa's voice, saying the words he had said to me years before when he had taught me to ride.

Pop and Mr. King were at the tractor, talking. Howdy and Earl stood a few feet away, waiting to hear their decision on the next step. But I knew that Grandpa was right. We couldn't give up—either of us.

I stood up, took a deep breath, and yelled fiercely, "Benny! Wake up! Get up! Get up, you old plug! Hey, you!"

Mr. King and Pop stopped talking and watched me. Earl and Howdy stared openly at this change in my behavior.

I stared as menacingly as I could and continued my unladylike tirade.

I turned one of the flashlights on him. Benny's eyelids popped open and he turned his head to look at me. As I roared louder a noticeable physical change took place in him: the old fire and determination shone in his eyes, burning out the weariness and resignation. He raised his head and even the familiar arch reappeared in his neck. Vitality flowed down that strong neck and through his muscles and nerves.

Mr. King jumped back on the tractor and Pop waved frantically for him to drive ahead before Benny changed his mind or gave up. The rope grew so taut Ben was straining for breath. But he neither lowered his head nor closed his eyes. As the pull of the rope twisted his head around toward the bank above him, he pulled his legs from the creek and began pawing viciously at the mud. He made no effort to stand, as any animal would normally have tried to do and as he had done before. Instead, he pushed and dug on his side as though swimming on top of the mud with the steady choking pull of the rope toward the edge of the bank.

I continued yelling at him, urging him on, telling him not to give up, that he was making it. Pop guided Mr. King with hand signals to show him when to move cautiously, when to stop for a minute, when to give a little slack.

Earl and Howdy stood at the edge of the bank, pulling for Benny, and joined me in shouting encouragement.

The rope, tight against Benny's windpipe, was wearing a small ditch in the upper edge of the soft bank. Ben's breathing was loud but he was still twisting, kicking, squirming, and maneuvering *with*, not against, the rope. Inch by inch his ears moved toward the wet grass at the top of the bank. The heavy drag of his body left a smooth path at the water's edge. Above it, the mud was torn, sliced, and gashed by his sharp hooves as he reached upward with each pull for solid ground.

Now Benny's ears showed over the edge of the bank. Howdy and Earl were on each side of him in a second and grabbed him under his jawbone and muscle to help pull him a little higher. Ben gasped for a swallow of air, seemed to collect himself, and with a final mighty heave brought up his right foreleg, then his left, so that his hooves were able to grab some fairly solid ground. A chunk of mud and grass broke off under the weight of his forelegs. He slid a little way down the bank again but managed to break the slide and regain the footing of his forelegs over the edge by twisting his hind legs into the surface of the mud along the top slope of the bank.

This time his forelegs held; his neck was bent over the edge on the wet grass. There was a tense and precarious second until Earl was able to wrap his arms under Benny's jaw and Howdy got his clasped hands under Ben's muzzle. Then both boys heaved backwards, their heels digging little trenches in the damp earth as they pulled. I tried to get a grip on Benny's ears but my hands were so muddy they slipped off as I tugged. I fell backwards on the ground. When I got up, I saw that Benny was out, though his hind legs hung over the bank.

Pop rushed forward and loosened the throttling rope from around Benny's neck. Mr. King ran to Benny's hindquarters. He and Earl each grabbed a hind leg and pulled it up into the air as Howdy and Pop pushed against Benny's shoulder until he was completely rolled over.

The heavy black mud was like a thick wrapping on every part of Ben. His mane and tail were matted; his whiskers held chunks of sod. He closed his eyes again and lay still, his breathing uneven. He lay on soft trampled ground but he would not sink in it when he was ready to stand. If he was able to stand . . .

"Just let him rest," Pop said gently. "He's exhausted."

"I hope he'll be all right," I whispered.

We were all almost as caked with mud and dirt as Benny. The mud on Pop's and the boys' faces was streaked with sweat; mine, I know, was streaked with tears—of fear and relief.

"I'd better have a look at him." Startled, I swung

around to see Dr. Conquest striding toward us with his big black case.

"Boy, are we glad to see you!" Howdy exclaimed.

"Mrs. Cline called me. I got here as soon as I could."

We told Dr. Conquest what had happened while he poked and prodded Benny, listened to his breathing, put a stethoscope to his heart, and shone a little flashlight into his eyes.

"It's a marvel that this old boy is still alive," he said.

The veterinarian pulled a syringe from his bag, filled it, and shot some fluid into a vein in Benny's neck. Then he took a small bottle from his bag, unscrewed the top, raised Benny's mouth skyward, and poured a generous dose down his throat. He held Ben's mouth shut until he was sure Ben had swallowed it.

"What was that?" I asked.

"Brandy," Doc replied. "It's a stimulant. Only thing to do now is to cover him up, let him rest awhile, and see if he wants to rejoin the horse race." Doc Conquest loved his little jokes and we all smiled dutifully.

"I'll go get a couple of blankets," Howdy volunteered.

"I'll take you up on the tractor," Mr. King said. "It's getting pretty dark and I've got chores to finish.

I don't think there's anything more I can do here anyway."

"Thanks an awful lot, Mr. King," I said. "I hate to think what might have happened to Benny if you hadn't been here to help."

Then I sat on the wet ground and cradled Benny's tired old head in my lap, stroking his face gently.

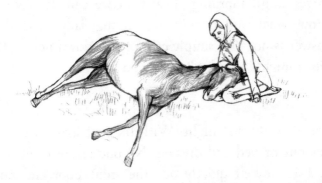

"I can't get over it," Doc Conquest said to Pop as Mr. King and the boys drove off in the tractor. "That horse must have a heart and constitution of iron. Most horses don't live to be his age in the first place and in the second place, if they did and got into the trouble he gets in, it would finish them off."

I knew, though. I knew Benny might not have much time left, but he wasn't going to go until he felt good and ready. I knew he wasn't ready yet.

"Will he be all right now?" Pop asked.

"It's up to Benny," Doc said. "This may have

taken a lot out of him. Have to wait a few days and see."

"Where'll I take care of him?" I asked. "It seems kind of damp and wet to leave him here."

"But Norma," Pop said, "we can't very well carry him up to the barn. As soon as Howdy gets back with the blankets, we'll cover him up and leave him here to rest until morning. That's all we can do. And I know what you're thinking, young lady, and the answer is no. You simply *cannot* stay down here with him tonight. We don't want you sick too."

I slept badly that night. With the first light of day I was out of bed and dressed. No one else was awake, so I let myself quietly out the front door and ran across to the barn. I decided I would skip Goldie's grain this morning; I was in too much of a hurry to get her bridle on and ride her down to Benny. As I started toward Goldie with the bridle, a welcoming whinny from under the walnut tree brought me to a dead stop. I peered between the slats of the white-washed fence.

"Benny!" I yelled. "What are *you* doing here? You're supposed to be down in the lower pasture, *recuperating*." I flew through the gate and flung myself at Benny. "You big crazy wonderful animal, you!"

Benny nuzzled me affectionately. His head hung low and his legs trembled with weakness but he was up. Somehow he had struggled the long way through the pastures during the night and made it to the barn.

I agreed with Doc Conquest: Benny, indeed, must have a heart and constitution of iron. But I also knew he had more than that—an unconquerable spirit.

Benny died in the spring of 1961. He died in his sleep, quietly and peacefully. Benny's heart never wavered until the end. His spirit never died.

No one lives on the farm now. The barn stands nearly empty, occupied only by wild fluttery pigeons, some mice and rats under the old oak floors, and a family of gophers. It has the smell of dusty hay, un-used straw and the faint musk of horse and cattle long since gone.

Tall weeds and prickly bushes grow high in the barnyard where once Benny and Goldie's flashing hooves and the cattle's cloven feet kept the ground bare. The stalls are empty and their gates hang open as though waiting for the return of their occupants. The pastures and the fields have been bitten into by con-struction equipment, leveling the rolling hills, throw-ing up embankments for a new superhighway that will cut across the farm. What fields are left on the flanks of the new expressway will be tilled by Mr. King. Their fertile soil will not lie fallow for a while yet.

The farmhouse, too, is almost empty. Mom and Pop have built a small comfortable house away from the noise of the traffic that will soon whiz across our fields. They will decide what they will do with the remaining land, the house and other buildings when the expressway is finished.

Grand Blanc is becoming a prosperous residential community, and there is a new, bigger high school. Houses and subdivisions circle the boundaries of our farm.

But what I see—and always will—is Benny, still galloping across the dusty pastures and through the woods. He dips his nose in the water trough under his walnut tree and flinches whenever a walnut drops on his back. He is stubborn and independent and nips at the seat of my jeans when I tighten his saddle girth. He chases Goldie. He nuzzles me for tidbits and pursues me for affection. He runs from me when he's angry and returns when I least expect him.

He does all these things and dozens more, over and over again, in my mind. And in my heart, Benny, who was thirty-three years old at his death, remains forever young.